# tech talk

**Intermediate**
Workbook

**Lewis Lansford**

**OXFORD**
UNIVERSITY PRESS

# Contents

# Unit 1

**1** Complete the introductions with the words in the list.

> stay  installed  working  installing  ~~work~~  design  install  travelling
> travel  develops  involves  built

I'm Mike Greenfield, and I .........._work_..........[1] for a company called Lights! We ...........................[2] and ...........................[3] exterior lighting systems for architectural applications – basically lights for the outside of big buildings. At the moment, we're ...........................[4] on new lighting for Durham Cathedral, in the North of England. Last year, we ...........................[5] a new lighting system outside the New York headquarters of South Asia Bank; that's a brand new building that has only just been ...........................[6] .

My name's Maria Santos. I'm a software engineer. I work for a company that ...........................[7] language recognition software. My work ...........................[8] developing products for the telecommunications industry. We sell our software all over the world, so I ...........................[9] a lot to meet clients. At the moment, my team is ...........................[10] a new system in Indonesia for their national mobile phone network. Several engineers will ...........................[11] there for about six months, but I am ...........................[12] back and forth regularly to keep an eye on the job and stay on top of my work in the office.

**2** Match a question or sentence on the left to a reply on the right.

1 What's your job? ————     a   Yes, I'm getting used to the new job, thanks.
2 How long have you been doing that?     b   OK, but it's taking longer than I expected.
3 Where do you work?     c   I have an apartment just outside Oslo.
4 Where do you live?     d   I'm designing a new application.
5 What languages do you speak?     e   I'm a quality control engineer.
6 How are you getting on with the plans?     f   In a factory near Jakarta.
7 What are you working on at the moment?     g   For about eighteen months.
8 Are you settling in OK?     h   English, Dutch, and Mandarin.

**3** Complete the sentences with the correct form of *have, do,* or *be.*

A What ....*do*....¹ you do?

B I ............² a mechanical engineer. What about you?

A I ............³ my own company. We provide computer training courses.

B Oh, really? How many employees ............⁴ there in your company?

A We ............⁵ six full-time and three part-time. Who do you work for?

B JJB. We make tractors. The company ............⁶ factories all over the world, so I travel a lot.

A Where have you ............⁷ recently?

B Well, I ............⁸ in Auckland, New Zealand, last month.

A Wow! ............⁹ you have a good time?

B Not really. I ............¹⁰ supposed to go to Oakland, in California. Somebody bought me a ticket to Auckland by mistake!

**4** Tick (✓) the sentences that are correct. Correct the sentences that are wrong.

     *aren't*
1 We ~~isn't~~ very busy right now.

2 I haven't had a holiday since 1994.

3 She don't work on Fridays.

4 Isn't he know he's not supposed to use his phone here?

5 Didn't we meet last year in Brussels?

6 We weren't very pleased with the quality of their product.

7 I doesn't know how to operate the new equipment.

8 He hasn't finished his project yet.

9 I'm don't sure when the guys from China are coming.

10 I not have my laptop with me today.

**5** Complete these emails using the words and phrases in the list.

> please   attached   best   confirm   ~~could you~~   could you please   be sure   contact
> I'm writing regarding   just a quick note to   let me know   regards   thank you

**a**

Gloria,

I keep forgetting to ask you this – .....*could you*..... [1] book this flight for me for the trip to Philadelphia:

Fri 8-Aug-08

Manchester (MAN) Depart 10:55 Terminal 2 to Philadelphia (PHL) Arrive 13:40 Terminal A

Duration: 7hr 45min

That will get us there in plenty of time for the start of the conference on Friday evening. The return flight can be whatever is available on the Monday.

........................... [2] wishes,

Alicia

**b**

Hello Adam,

........................... [3] let you know I'll be in Spain from tomorrow until Friday, 30 April. If you need anything while I'm away, ........................... [4] Simon Parker on 07190 962 344. He'll know how to reach me. I'll call you when I get back.

Best ........................... [5],

Sarah-Jane

**c**

Dear Mr Dureau

........................... [6] our phone call today about the shipment of non-kink polypropylene drain hoses that were the wrong length. As we agreed on the phone, ........................... [7] send the replacements for arrival this Friday and arrange for collection of the wrong hoses. Please send an exchange note to Abigail Brooks in purchasing and ........................... [8] that there will be no handling fee.

........................... [9] for your help.

Elliot Bliss

**d**

Hi everyone,

........................... [10] is a tentative agenda for Friday's monthly planning meeting. As you can see, we have a lot to get through, so ........................... [11] to show up on time (for a change!). And ........................... [12] if you have any changes.

Cheers,

Betsy

**6** Which message above:

1 is the most formal? ........

2 asks someone to correct a mistake? ........

3 tells someone how they can be contacted? ........

4 includes a document in addition to the email message? ........

**7** From these eight email subject headings, choose one that matches each of the email messages below.

> Short break   ~~Bad news, mate~~   Order number 99032: shipping delay   Refund notice
> Cancellation of order number 88901   Corrected order (replacement parts)
> Re: 100 cases of paper?!   Replacement shipped yesterday

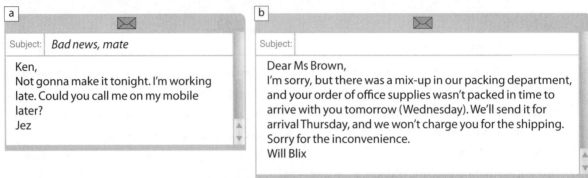

**a**

Subject: *Bad news, mate*

Ken,
Not gonna make it tonight. I'm working late. Could you call me on my mobile later?
Jez

**b**

Subject:

Dear Ms Brown,
I'm sorry, but there was a mix-up in our packing department, and your order of office supplies wasn't packed in time to arrive with you tomorrow (Wednesday). We'll send it for arrival Thursday, and we won't charge you for the shipping. Sorry for the inconvenience.
Will Blix

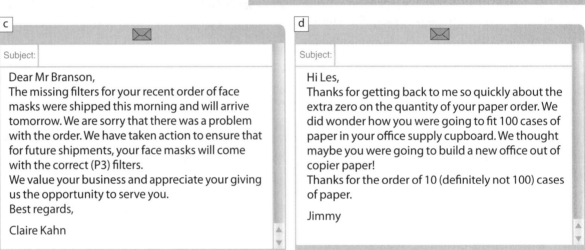

**c**

Subject:

Dear Mr Branson,
The missing filters for your recent order of face masks were shipped this morning and will arrive tomorrow. We are sorry that there was a problem with the order. We have taken action to ensure that for future shipments, your face masks will come with the correct (P3) filters.
We value your business and appreciate your giving us the opportunity to serve you.
Best regards,

Claire Kahn

**d**

Subject:

Hi Les,
Thanks for getting back to me so quickly about the extra zero on the quantity of your paper order. We did wonder how you were going to fit 100 cases of paper in your office supply cupboard. We thought maybe you were going to build a new office out of copier paper!
Thanks for the order of 10 (definitely not 100) cases of paper.

Jimmy

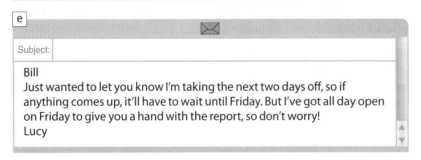

**e**

Subject:

Bill
Just wanted to let you know I'm taking the next two days off, so if anything comes up, it'll have to wait until Friday. But I've got all day open on Friday to give you a hand with the report, so don't worry!
Lucy

**8** Which message(s) in **7**:

1 apologizes? ....*b*....

2 give bad news? ........ ........ ........

3 offers help? ........

4 thanks someone for something? ........

5 requests action? ........

6 passes on information? ........

# Unit 2

**1** Look at the diagram and picture of a boat that is used for installing wind turbines in the sea. Write numbers to complete the text below.

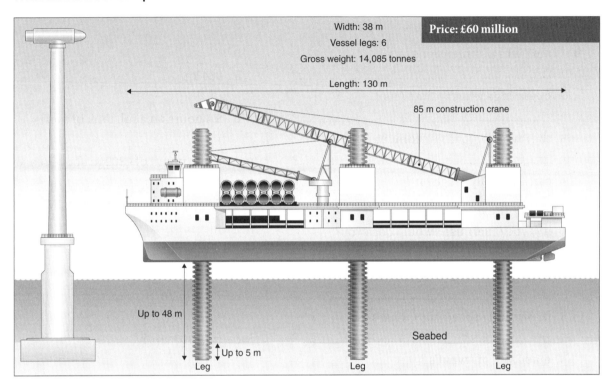

Width: 38 m
Vessel legs: 6
Gross weight: 14,085 tonnes

**Price: £60 million**

Length: 130 m

85 m construction crane

Up to 48 m

Up to 5 m

Leg

Leg

Seabed

Leg

Most boats do not have legs. But a jack-up barge has .............6.............[1]. When the ship is moving, the legs stand high in the air. When the ship stops to install the foundations for a wind turbine, the legs extend to a length of ...........................[2] m below the ship and penetrate to a depth of ...........................[3] m into the seabed. The boat is ...........................[4] m wide, ...........................[5] m long, and the length of its crane is ...........................[6] m. It weighs ...........................[7] tonnes. Made in China, it cost £ ...........................[8] million.

It's a big job installing turbines. The installation time for foundations is usually ...........................[9] hours, and when they're working, turbines can be ...........................[10] m tall.

It usually takes 24 to 36 hours to install wind turbine foundations from a vessel like the Resolution. Wind turbines often stand 125 metres above the sea.

**2** Unscramble the questions. Then match each question to an answer.

A  1  it / to / did / build / how / take / long?
   *How long did it take to build?*

   2  it / cost / how / much / does ?
   ..............................................................................?

   3  much / weigh / how / it / does ?
   ..............................................................................?

   4  tank / capacity / the / what's / fuel ?
   ..............................................................................?

   a  90 kg

   b  9 L

   c  1,800 hours

   d  €750

B  1  are / what / dimensions / its ?
   ..............................................................................?

   2  operating / what's / time / its ?
   ..............................................................................?

   3  the / what's / load / maximum ?
   ..............................................................................?

   4  can / how / fly / high / it ?
   ..............................................................................?

   a  364 kg

   b  5.4 hours on a full tank of fuel

   c  a maximum of 4800 m above sea level

   d  6 m (L) x 1.7 m (H) x 9.75 m (W)

C  1  it / type / fuel / use / what / does / of ?
   ..............................................................................?

   2  it / what / does / of / type / engine / have ?
   ..............................................................................?

   3  maximum / speed / its / what's ?
   ..............................................................................?

   4  made / it / of / what's ?
   ..............................................................................?

   a  wood

   b  4.6 litre V8

   c  over 300 km/h

   d  unleaded petrol

**3** Match each picture below to a set of specifications (A–C) in **2**.

**4** Match each feature with a unit of measurement.

| | | |
|---|---|---|
| 1 rotation speed | a | bar |
| 2 memory | b | L/h |
| 3 temperature | c | V |
| 4 pressure | d | rpm |
| 5 voltage | e | °C |
| 6 water output | f | MB |

**5** Use the words in the list to complete the descriptions of three products.

> grows  rotates  plug  damage  recharge
> see  use  ~~worry~~  store  has  tells  put

## Vehicle battery booster

It plugs directly into the vehicle's DC outlet, so you don't have to
.......*worry*.......[1] about getting out of the car.

It's very compact, so it's easy to ...........................[2]. It doesn't
require cables, so it's very easy to ...........................[3].

It ...........................[4] a built-in, ultra-bright LED light for night-
time emergency roadside assistance. There's a 12-volt DC outlet to
...........................[5] mobile phone batteries.

## Towel pill

This tiny pill is actually an extremely compressed towel.

When it's dry, it's tiny and easy to ...........................[6] in your
pocket or purse. When it gets wet, it ...........................[7] into a
40 cm x 40 cm towel that you can use to wash your face or clean
up unexpected messes.

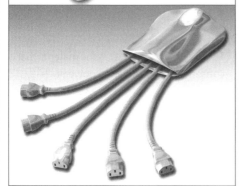

## The squid

Surge protection means dangerous power surges and
electrical spikes won't ...........................[8] your electronic equipment.

Two blue neon glowing outlets make it easy to ...........................[9]
and safe to use in the dark. The plug ...........................[10] through
360 degrees, making it easy to use in small or awkward spaces.
An audible alarm ...........................[11] you when it's time to replace
it, so you'll always be protected. Flexible outlets make it easy to
...........................[12] in a lot of bulky plugs.

**6** In the descriptions above, put a <u>single underline</u> under the features and a <u>double underline</u> under the benefits.

**7** Match each description of a benefit to a feature.

1 It's light, so it's easy to move.          a  cost
2 105 bar output makes cleaning easy.        b  size
3 It's carbon neutral.                       c  weight
4 It's made from attractive leather.         d  construction materials
5 It's easy to store because it's compact.   e  greenhouse gas emissions
6 It's affordable.                           f  pressure

**8** Complete the crossword.

**Across**

3 Many products offer several ...................... for some features, for example size and colour.

7 Manufacturers usually offer a ...................... that says they will repair or replace a product if it breaks within a certain time after purchase.

8 ...................... can be expressed in square metres.

9 The ...................... of a product is the amount of time that it remains useful before it wears out.

10 A product's exterior ...................... material is the material, for example leather, that covers the outside of the product.

11 A product's ...................... are descriptions of its size, weight, capacity, and other features.

15 Something that weighs a lot can be described as ...................... .

17 A product's ...................... are often given as height, length, and depth.

18 If a product saves time, that means it works more ...................... than other products.

19 The quality of a photographic image can be described in terms of ...................... .

20 A product's ...................... are the things that make it helpful and useful.

**Down**

1 The fuel ...................... is the material that is consumed by a product to power it.

2 ...................... speed is the speed at which something turns round and round.

4 The ...................... materials are the materials that a product is made of.

5 The ...................... temperature of a product is the temperature that it normally works at, after it has warmed up.

6 If something doesn't fall over easily, it can be described as ...................... .

10 The ...................... of a product is a description of what it's made of.

12 ...................... is the volume of a substance, for example fuel, that a container will hold.

13 A product's ...................... are the things that the product can do.

14 A vehicle's ...................... possible speed is called top speed.

16 One way to describe a benefit of a product is to say what ...................... it solves.

# Unit 3

**1** Complete the sentences with the words in the list.

When   Next   ~~Make sure~~   After   Finally   First

a  .........*Make sure*......... that the edge of the pond is the same level all around.  ........
b  ..............................the pond is full, cut the liner to fit.  ........
c  .............................., dig a hole the size and shape you want your pond to be.  ...1...
d  .............................., line the hole with damp sand.  ........
e  .............................., put stones around the edge of the pond to complete it.  ........
f  ..............................that, put the liner in the pond and fill it with water.  ........

**2** Look at the pictures. Number the instructions in **1** in order.

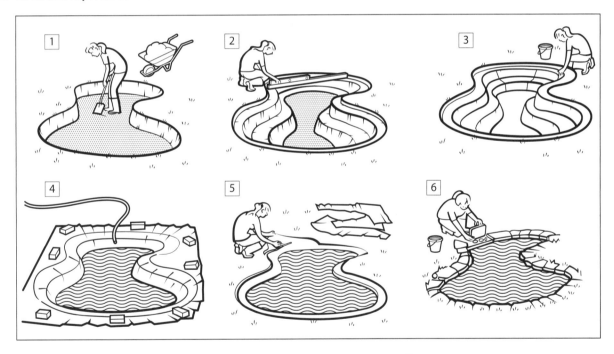

**3** Match each of these additional instructions to a main instruction in **1**.

1  ..*b*.. Be careful not to cut too much off.
2  ...... You may want to make a square pond rather than a round one.
3  ...... It's essential to do this. Otherwise, stones may damage the liner when you put it in.
4  ...... This is important, as the pond won't look nice with one edge higher than the others.
5  ...... Once you've done this, you can sit back and enjoy your finished pond!
6  ...... It's important to fill it as full as possible because the water will stretch the pond liner.

**4** Read the text about choosing fish. Then match each step to a description below.

## Choosing the right fish for your pond

1 Before you consider putting fish in your pond, check the water temperature and quality. Set up a water filter and circulation system to keep the water fresh.

2 Don't rush to put a lot of fish in, or else you may be sorry.

3 Once your pond is ready, put in just one fish. This one fish will help prepare the water to support more fish by encouraging the growth of bacteria that break down fish waste.

4 It's best to choose a fish that is well suited to your environment. You can choose fancy, rare fish, but they may not live for very long.

5 Just before adding more fish, buy a water test kit to make sure the water is OK.

6 It's essential that you don't let fallen leaves build up at the bottom of the pond. They produce hydrogen sulphide gas that will kill your fish.

a ...6... This step is necessary.

b ........ One step must be completed before another can happen.

c ........ One step immediately follows another.

d ........ This step is advisable but not necessary.

e ........ You shouldn't do this.

f ........ This is necessary preparation.

**5** Match the sentence halves.

| | |
|---|---|
| 1 For your car's cooling system, distilled water's best, | a so be careful not to touch it or you'll burn yourself. |
| 2 Switch the iron on | b otherwise the water won't drain off. |
| 3 When the water in the kettle is hot enough, | c and to work on one strip at a time. |
| 4 After you install the software, | d but it's not essential. |
| 5 Make sure there is plenty of gravel in the bottom, | e or else your subject won't relax. |
| 6 The plate gets very hot, | f the light goes off. |
| 7 It's best to work downwards | g and wait a few minutes for it to warm up. |
| 8 Be careful to speak softly, | h you have to restart your computer. |

**6** Look at the picture. Use the words in the list to label the parts.

> ball  bell  boxing glove  chain  chute  cigarette lighter  doorbell button
> flame  hammer  pulley  rope  scissors  string  trap door  weight

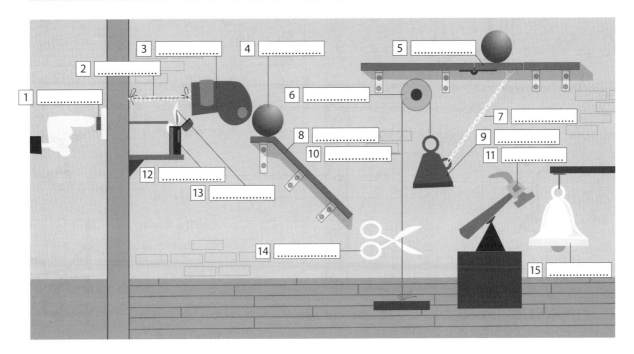

**7** Rewrite the sentences using *which*.

1 This is the doorbell button. It lights the cigarette lighter.
........................*This is the doorbell button which lights the cigarette lighter.*........................

2 This is the flame. It burns the string.
..........................................................................................................

3 The broken string releases the boxing glove. The boxing glove hits the ball.
..........................................................................................................

4 There's a chute. The ball rolls down the chute.
..........................................................................................................

5 This is the rope. It goes over a pulley.
..........................................................................................................

6 The ball hits the scissors. The scissors cut the rope.
..........................................................................................................

7 There's a weight. It drops when the rope is cut.
..........................................................................................................

8 There's a trap door. It's pulled open by the chain when the weight drops.
..........................................................................................................

9 Resting on the trap door there's a ball. It falls when the door opens.
..........................................................................................................

10 The falling ball hits a hammer. The hammer rings the bell.
..........................................................................................................

## 8 Complete the puzzle.

1 The siphon ...... the candle.

2 You pull the ...... .

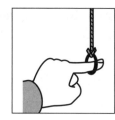

3 The spoon ...... .

4 The boxing glove ...... the plunger.

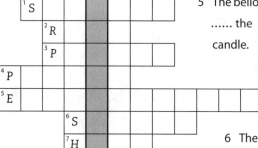

| | | | | | | | | |
|---|---|---|---|---|---|---|---|---|
| ¹S | | | | | | | | |
| ²R | | | | | | | | |
| ³P | | | | | | | | |
| ⁴P | | | | | | | | |
| ⁵E | | | | | | | | |
| ⁶S | | | | | | | | |
| ⁷H | | | | | | | | |
| ⁸L | | | | | | | | |
| ⁹P | | | | | | | | |

5 The bellows ...... the candle.

6 The scissors cut the ...... .

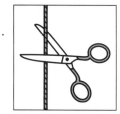

7 The hammer ...... the nail.

8 The hook catches the ...... .

9 You ...... the jug under the tap.

## 9 Unscramble the definitions.

1 at / tube / that / end / funnel / is / is / wide / A / one / a

*A funnel is a tube that is wide at one end.*
....................................................................................

2 piece / A / a / equipment / bellows / air / is / of / that / blows

....................................................................................

3 on / blade / edge / cutting / A / is / a / flat / a / knife

....................................................................................

4 lid / box / which / A / is / a / has / tray / no / shallow

....................................................................................

5 wheel / gear / is / has / which / A / a / teeth

....................................................................................

6 that / liquid / A / a / tank / holds / is / container

....................................................................................

# Unit 4

**1** Complete the descriptions of helpful tips and suggested fixes with the words in the list.

run ~~move~~ soak wipe dissolve shield prevent

1 When a bolt is stuck and won't .............*move*............., we cut it off with a grinder and replace it.

2 After spraying on the adhesive, use a cloth to ......................... away the extra liquid.

3 We use a light coating of grease on exposed metal parts to ......................... against rust during shipping.

4 We use this glue because it's permanent – you can't ......................... it with anything!

5 Don't rush. Wait a few minutes for the liquid to ......................... into the surface.

6 The best way to ......................... rust on the blade is to keep it clean and dry.

7 Every day, we oil the spindle on our table grinder so it will ......................... smoothly.

**2** Mr Fixit works in four ways. For each benefit described below, write C (cleans), P (protects), L (lubricates), or D (displaces moisture).

1 ...P.... Shields metal surfaces from moisture and other corrosive elements.

2 ......... Keeps moving parts running smoothly.

3 ......... Gets under dirt and grease, making it easy to wipe them away.

4 ......... Loosens and frees metal parts that are stuck.

5 ......... Dissolves adhesives, making it easy to remove tape and sticky labels.

6 ......... Prevents rust and corrosion.

7 ......... Soaks into rust.

8 ......... Dries out electrical systems and prevents short circuits.

**3** Choose the best word to complete each sentence.

1 The distributor was ..............*wet*............., so I dried it with Mr Fixit.
   a wet        b cold        c rusty

2 I use it on the car's locks to stop them ................................. in winter.
   a working    b freezing    c budging

3 We tried ................................. the labels, but they were firmly stuck.
   a fixing     b peeling     c sticking

4 I pulled the bike seat, but it was so ................................. it wouldn't budge.
   a rusty      b noisy       c soaked

5 The fan cooled the room, but the ................................. kept us awake at night.
   a rust       b heat        c noise

6 We ................................. the fan to make it quieter.
   a raised     b cooled      c lubricated

**4** Match each situation with an effect.

1 The glass was so dirty,          a we couldn't peel it off.
2 The scissors were so rusty,       b he couldn't put the key in it.
3 The window was so firmly stuck,   c he couldn't find the end of it.
4 The bolt was so rusty,            d we couldn't sleep.
5 The label was so firmly stuck,    e you couldn't use them.
6 The fan made so much noise,       f I couldn't see through it.
7 The lock was so frozen,           g he couldn't open it.
8 The rope was so tangled,          h we couldn't turn it.

**5** Match each sentence in **4** to the correct picture below.

**6** Number the sentences to complete the story.

a ........ It was still very hard to open and close, so I squirted even more Mr Fixit inside.

b ........ But I still can't go anywhere. When I checked the tyres, one of them was flat!

c ...1... I didn't use my bike all winter. In spring, the lock was rusted shut.

d ........ I soaked it in Mr Fixit and left it for a while.

e ........ I sprayed on some more Mr Fixit and loosened it some more.

f ........ That did the trick. The lock now works perfectly.

g ........ It wouldn't budge.

h ........ A little later, I gave it a tug and it moved.

**7** Look at the pictures showing a movie-making process. Number the steps.

# Rotoscoping

When makers of animated films want their characters to move like real people, they often begin work by using actors. The technique is called rotoscoping, and it can be done with a software application called Rotoshop. Here's how it works.

a ....... Finally, the completed scenes are processed by the computer. This process, called rendering, prepares the sequences for copying to film.

b ....... After that, animation artists use digital pens to trace the actors on the photographs. When there is movement, the first and final positions are traced, and powerful computer software fills in the gaps.

c ...1... First, every shot in the film is carefully planned. This is usually done by creating a storyboard, which is a series of pictures like a comic that tells the story of the film.

d ....... The next step is to add scenery and colour. For a complex scene, this step can take weeks to complete.

e ....... Next, actors are placed in the correct positions and photographed with digital cameras. Because the backgrounds will be added later by animators, they don't need to be included in the photos.

**8** Underline nine examples of the passive voice in the text in **7**.

**9** Change the active to the passive if possible. If it's not possible, put a cross (✗).

1 Simone sent an email message.
...................*An email message was sent by Simone.*...................................

2 A strange thing happened in the computer lab.
......................................................................................................................

3 Philip designed the machine that produces the new parts.
......................................................................................................................

4 Eloise explained the production process.
......................................................................................................................

5 It rained all day on Friday.
......................................................................................................................

6 Adam answered the questions at the end of the presentation.
......................................................................................................................

7 Helen signed the contract.
......................................................................................................................

8 Everyone seemed happy after the meeting.
......................................................................................................................

9 All of us enjoyed a successful year.
......................................................................................................................

10 The workstation caught fire.
......................................................................................................................

**10** Do the sentences give not enough information, the right amount, or too much? For each sentence, tick (✓) the correct box.

|  | not enough | the right amount | too much |
|---|---|---|---|
| 1 The fire was caused. | ✓ | | |
| 2 The fire was caused by a faulty wire. | | | |
| 3 The new warehouse will be completed next month. | | | |
| 4 The new warehouse will be completed next month by the builders. | | | |
| 5 Was this message written? | | | |
| 6 Was this message written by Steve? | | | |
| 7 Rice is grown in Thailand. | | | |
| 8 Rice is grown in Thailand by people. | | | |
| 9 That museum is visited. | | | |
| 10 That museum is visited by thousands of people every day. | | | |

# Unit 5

**1** Complete the short conversations using the words and phrases in the list.

> appreciate   can   can I   could you   do you need a hand   ~~I'm afraid~~   it was a pleasure
> nice to see   no problem   sorry   take   thank   thanks   that's very kind
> was great seeing you   yes   yes, of course

1 JIM   Hello?

    JO   Hi, Jim. It's Jo. Listen, ............*I'm afraid*............[1] I'm running about twenty minutes late.

    JIM   OK, thanks for letting me know. Where are you?

    JO   I'm on I-10, just at Congress Street.

    JIM   Listen, Jo, Congress is closed ...

    JO   Oh, ................................[2] you for letting me know.

    JIM   ... so you should ................................[3] the Broadway exit.

    JO   OK, got it. I'm just there now.

2 JIM   Hey, ................................[4] you!

    JO   Hi, Jim. ................................[5] I'm late.

    JIM   No problem. ................................[6] with that box?

    JO   Yes, I'd ................................[7] it.

    JIM   And ................................[8] get you a cup of coffee?

    JO   ................................[9], please. Milk, no sugar.

3 JIM   It's been good talking with you, Jo.

    JO   Yes, it's been great. ................................[10] you send me the estimate next week?

    JIM   ................................[11]. As soon as I've worked out the costs.

    JO   Great. And ................................[12] send a rough schedule, too?

    JIM   Sure.

4 JO   How do I get back to my car from here?

    JIM   I'll come with you.

    JO   Oh, ................................[13] of you.

    JIM   ................................[14].

5 JIM   We'll be in touch.

    JO   Yes, definitely. ................................[15] for everything.

    JIM   ................................[16].

    JO   Well, it ................................[17].

    JIM   Bye! Take care!

## 2 Match each picture to a label.

1 They're greeting each other. ...*h*...

2 They're saying goodbye. ........

3 She's offering physical help. ........

4 He's saying thank you. ........

5 He's asking for directions. ........

6 He's saying he's sorry. ........

7 She's giving directions. ........

8 He's offering to do something. ........

## 3 Now choose the best response to each situation in 2.

1 Nice to meet you, too. ...*h*...

2 Yes, I'll call you next week. ........

3 No, thanks. I can manage. ........

4 You're welcome. ........

5 Sure, no problem. ........

6 Don't worry about it. ........

7 OK, turn right at the corner ... ........

8 Thanks. I'm completely lost! ........

**4** Complete the story using the words in the lists.

## Tracking the writer of Melissa

~~lots~~ the some many few

When the Melissa computer virus was released in 1999, it very quickly caused ..........lots.......... [1] of problems on the internet. It spread very quickly via email, and .......................... [2] computer networks were shut down by the virus before it could be stopped. .......................... [3] people who create internet viruses are ever caught, but this time the writer of the virus was caught only a few days after the virus was released. How was it done?

The virus was first noticed by virus detection software. Almost immediately, .......................... [4] FBI hired .......................... [5] America Online techies to troubleshoot. In addition, users from the alt.comp.virus newsgroup began to hunt for the writer of the virus.

a lot  other  several  all  a few  another

At the same time, in Massachusetts, software company president Richard M Smith looked closely at .......................... [6] viruses that had been posted using the same email address. He shared .......................... [7] of the information he could find with .......................... [8] expert, computer-science student Fredrik Bjorck. Bjorck said that the Melissa virus had .......................... [9] of features similar to the work of a virus writer called VicodinES (his 'working' name; no one knew his real identity). Smith then visited Vicodin's website, where he was able to download .......................... [10] virus writing tool kits. He looked closely at the source code of the software and made an amazing discovery: the name David L Smith appeared.......................... [11] times in the code.

any  millions  couple  a little  much

The AOL techies, with .......................... [12] help from the FBI, were able to find the specific telephone that was used to upload the virus. It belonged to David L Smith. A .......................... [13] of hours later, the police arrested Smith. He was eventually jailed.

It didn't take the virus .......................... [14] time to cause .......................... [15] of dollars in damage. Fortunately, the authorities didn't waste .......................... [16] time tracking down the writer of Melissa.

**5** Are these nouns from the article about Melissa countable (C) or uncountable (U)? Tick (✓) the right column.

| | C | U |
|---|---|---|
| 1 virus | ✓ | |
| 2 problem | | |
| 3 internet | | |
| 4 network | | |
| 5 software | | |
| 6 address | | |
| 7 information | | |
| 8 email | | |

**6** Match the pairs of sentences with the same meaning.

1 Neither of the spare parts worked.
2 We have several spare parts.
3 None of the spare parts worked.
4 There are loads of computers.
5 There's little time to rest.
6 Turn off all of the computers.
7 Turn off both computers.
8 There's a little time to rest.
9 We have plenty of spare parts.
10 There are too many computers.

a There's a short time, but enough to rest.
b There are three or more computers – turn them off.
c There were two spare parts, but they didn't do the job.
d There are more computers than necessary.
e There are two computers – turn them off.
f We have all the spare parts we need.
g There were three or more spare parts, but they didn't do the job.
h We don't have enough time to rest.
i There is a large number of computers.
j We have some spare parts, but not a lot.

**7** Look at the calendar. For each sentence below, circle T (true) or F (false).

| June | July | August | September |
|---|---|---|---|
| 3 people visited. 1 mm rain Bought a new computer (£699). | 2 people visited. 930 mm rain Bought a new car (£13,599). | 1,150 people visited. 0 mm rain Moved to a new location. | Now! |

1 We had a few visitors in June. (T)/ F

2 In June, we had little rain. T / F

3 We had few visitors in July. T / F

4 We spent little money in July. T / F

5 In August, we had few visitors. T / F

6 We had a little rain in August. T / F

7 A few months ago, we moved to a new location. T / F

8 We bought a new computer a few months ago. T / F

# Unit 6

**1** Complete the conversation using the words and phrases in the list.

> ~~we won't be able to start work on time~~   I won't let you come to work tomorrow
> we won't be able to get our truck on to the site   they've widened it
> we have to take it down ourselves   they'll have to widen the door

OMAR   OK, let's go over this one more time. Is the site ready for us to start work tomorrow?

BERNIE   Adam said it is, and he's in charge there.

OMAR   If they haven't prepared the site, ........... *we won't be able to start work on time* ...........[1].
And we're already behind schedule.

BERNIE   Well, we gave them clear instructions. Adam says
everything's ready.

OMAR   What about the access? If they haven't taken down
the fence, ...................................................................[2].

BERNIE   Don't worry, it was on the list.

OMAR   But has it been done?

BERNIE   I don't know. Let's take all the tools we need in case
...................................................................[3].

OMAR   Do they know about the size of the door?

BERNIE   The door?

OMAR   Yes. We won't be able to get the compressor in unless
...................................................................[4].

BERNIE   Listen, Omar, it was in the plan. It'll be OK. And if there's a problem getting
the compressor in, ...................................................................[5].

OMAR   But will they be able to do that?

BERNIE   They'll have to do it. But don't worry, Omar. It was all in the plans. It'll be OK. If you
don't stop worrying so much, ...................................................................[6]!

**2** Match the sentence halves.

1 The site
2 Adam
3 Bernie
4 Omar
5 The fence
6 The door
7 Instructions
8 The plans

a  is worried that the site won't be ready.
b  showed exactly how wide the door needed to be.
c  needs to be wide enough for the compressor to go in.
d  were given for how to prepare the site.
e  wouldn't allow the trucks to drive on to the site.
f  needs to be ready for work to start tomorrow.
g  is in charge of the site.
h  thinks the site will be ready.

**3** Look at the flow chart. Complete the sentences.

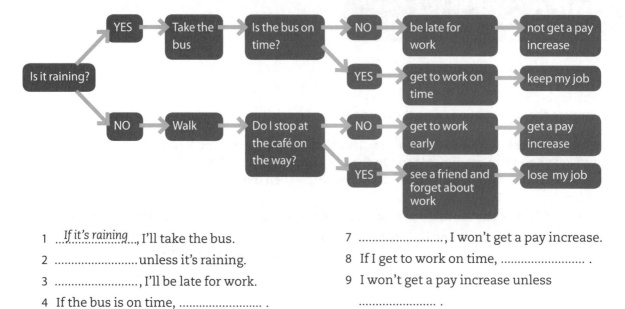

1  ...*If it's raining*..., I'll take the bus.
2  ........................unless it's raining.
3  ........................, I'll be late for work.
4  If the bus is on time, ........................ .
5  I'll get to work early unless ........................ .
6  If I stop at the café on the way, ........................ .

7  ........................, I won't get a pay increase.
8  If I get to work on time, ........................ .
9  I won't get a pay increase unless
   ........................ .
10 If I see a friend and forget about work,
   ........................ .

**4** Match each picture to a sentence.

1  ...*d*....  If it rains, I won't go out.
2  .........  I'll take an umbrella in case it rains.
3  .........  I won't take an umbrella unless it's raining.
4  .........  I'll take an umbrella if it's raining.

**5** Look at the information about three cars. Use the words in the list to complete the sentences.

**Cycle car**

| | |
|---|---|
| weight: | 55 kg |
| top speed: | approx 50 km/h |
| fuel consumption: | 0 |
| $CO_2$ emissions: | 0 |

**4WD**

| | |
|---|---|
| weight: | 2,200 kg |
| top speed: | 150 km/h |
| fuel consumption: | 20 mpg (11.7 l/100km) |
| $CO_2$ emissions: | 325 g/km |

**Hybrid**

| | |
|---|---|
| weight: | 1,250 kg |
| top speed: | 170 km/h |
| fuel consumption: | 65.7 mpg (4.3 l/100km) |
| $CO_2$ emissions: | 110 g/km |

> most   best   ~~less~~   much lower   slightly higher
> smallest   much more   better   worst   most

1 The Hybrid uses ............. *less* ............. fuel than the 4WD.
2 The 4WD emits the ...................................... $CO_2$.
3 The top speed of the cycle car is ...................................... than the top speed of the hybrid.
4 The cycle car is the ...................................... environmentally friendly.
5 The top speed of the hybrid is ...................................... than the top speed of the 4WD.
6 The cycle car has the ...................................... carbon footprint of the three cars.
7 The 4WD weighs ...................................... than the cycle car.
8 The cycle car is definitely the ...................................... for the environment.
9 The 4WD is probably the ...................................... for the environment.
10 The hybrid is ...................................... for the environment than the 4WD.

**6** For each sentence, circle T (true) or F (false).

1 The 4WD is slightly heavier than the cycle car.              T / (F)
2 The cycle car is the most harmful for the environment.       T / F
3 The hybrid is the fastest of the three cars.                 T / F
4 The hybrid is worse for the environment than the cycle car.  T / F
5 The $CO_2$ emissions of the 4WD are a lot lower than the hybrid. T / F
6 The slowest of the three cars is the most fuel efficient.    T / F

**7 Complete the puzzle.**

How to reduce your carbon footprint

1 Switch to ............................cleaning products.
2 Stop ............................mail.
3 ............................less.
4 Stop ............................new books.
5 Use a push ............................to cut the grass.
6 Eat meat-free meals every ............................day.
7 Install more ............................in your house.
8 Take a holiday at ............................ .
9 Take ............................flights.
10 ............................off appliances when you aren't using them.
11 Choose ............................with less packaging.
12 Be aware of your impact on the ............................ .

**8 Read the suggestions in 7 above. Answer the questions.**

1 Which one are you most likely to do?
2 Which one are you least likely to do?
3 Which one do you think is the hardest to do?
4 Which one is the easiest?

# Unit 7

**1  Look at the signs. Choose the sentence that best explains each rule.**

a  You're allowed to drive at 40 km an hour.
b  You can't use this road.
c  You have to drive 40 km an hour.
d  You don't need to do anything unless your vehicle is wide.
e  You don' t need to smoke.
f  You don't need to drive carefully because the road bends.
g  You aren't allowed to smoke.
h  You shouldn't wear eye protection.
i  You must wear eye protection.
j  You ought to drive carefully because the road bends.

k  You mustn't turn right.
l  You don't have to bring a dog in with you.
m  You don't have to wash your hands.
n  You ought to turn left.
o  You have to turn left.
p  You mustn't go faster than 20 km an hour.
q  You can't bring a dog in with you.
r  You should turn left.
s  You should wash your hands.
t  You can't stop if other cars are coming.
u  You should go at least 20 km an hour.
v  You don't have to stop unless other cars are coming.

**2** Look at the rules for carry-on items. Use the words in the list to complete the conversations.

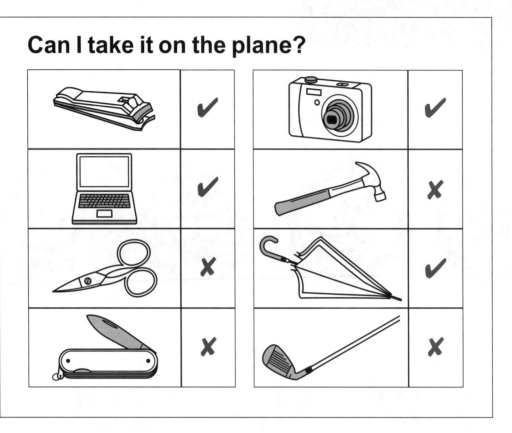

## Can I take it on the plane?

allowed   don't have to   mustn't   can   shouldn't   need   can't   should   have to

A Am I .......*allowed*........¹ to bring this laptop on board?

B Yes, but I'm afraid you ...................² take that golf club!

A ...............................³ I pack this camera in my suitcase?

B No, you ...............................⁴ take it in your hand luggage.

A Oh, sorry. Do I ...............................⁵ to leave these nail clippers here?

B No, but you'll ...............................⁶ leave that knife.

A Sorry, you ...............................⁷ take that hammer on board. You ...............................⁸ have those scissors, either.

B Oh, sorry.

A You ...........................⁹ worry about that umbrella. It's not a problem.

B Oh, good!

**3** On what page would you find each of the illustrations a–e?

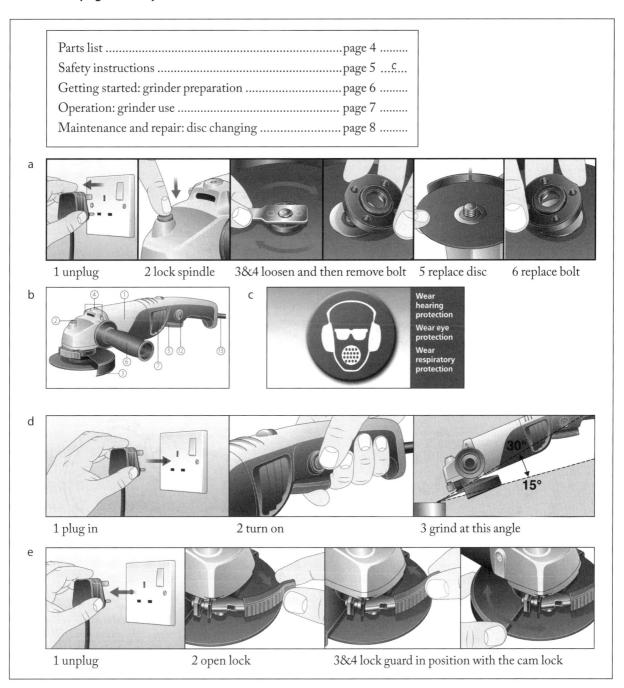

a

1 unplug    2 lock spindle    3&4 loosen and then remove bolt    5 replace disc    6 replace bolt

b

c
Wear hearing protection
Wear eye protection
Wear respiratory protection

d

1 plug in    2 turn on    3 grind at this angle

e

1 unplug    2 open lock    3&4 lock guard in position with the cam lock

**4** What do the pictures in **3** show? Match the nouns to make noun phrases.

| picture | noun phrase | |
|---|---|---|
| a1 | 1 power | a equipment |
| a3 | 2 changing | b disc |
| a5 | 3 grinding | c socket |
| b | 4 angle | d grinder |
| c | 5 safety | e tool |
| d3 | 6 grinding | f angle |

**5** Use noun phrases to describe these pictures.

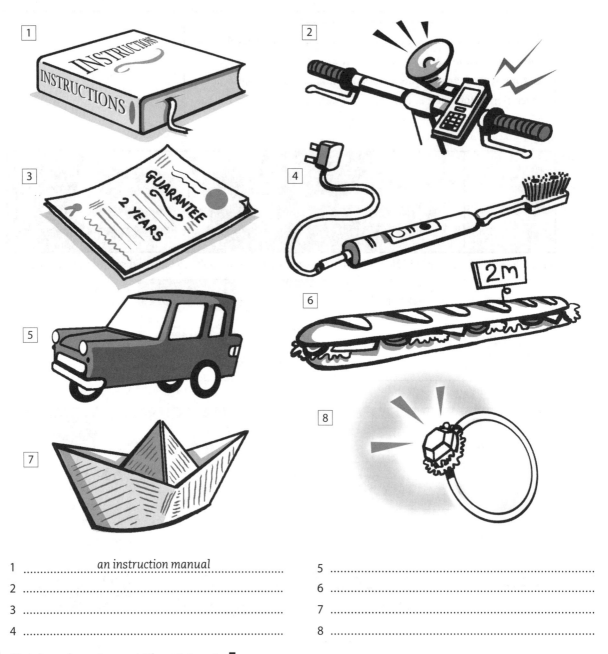

1 ........................ *an instruction manual* ........................
2 ................................................................................
3 ................................................................................
4 ................................................................................

5 ................................................................................
6 ................................................................................
7 ................................................................................
8 ................................................................................

**6** Match each sentence with a picture in **5**.

a ...2.... I like it because I don't have to stop riding to make a call.

b ........ After I've made it, I can sail it in the bath.

c ........ I don't have to spend so much money on tyres.

d ........ You must be very careful not to lose it. It's small, but very valuable.

e ........ I have to use this a lot because the machine is new.

f ........ The company that made it has to repair or replace it if there's a problem.

g ........ I need a place to plug this in.

h ........ You shouldn't try to eat this all at once.

# Unit 8

**1** Look at the pictures. Which worker is:

1 using an efficient lifting technique? ...*b*...      3 taking an unnecessary risk? .........

2 using an inefficient lifting technique? .........      4 using improper equipment? .........

**2** Read the text. Circle T (true) or F (false).

According to the text:

| | | |
|---|---|---|
| 1 | Boxes should never be lifted manually. | T / **F** |
| 2 | Using a fork-lift often leads to increased back injuries. | T / F |
| 3 | A fork-lift is usually safer than manual lifting. | T / F |
| 4 | Not keeping a workspace tidy can cause accidents. | T / F |
| 5 | Trying to carry too much weight is a common cause of fork-lift accidents. | T / F |
| 6 | Improper maintenance can lead to breakdowns and accidents. | T / F |
| 7 | One problem with fork-lifts is driver discomfort. | T / F |
| 8 | Improper training can lead to improved workplace safety. | T / F |

## Safe lifting

Improper and inefficient lifting in warehouses can cause injuries, so where it's possible, a fork-lift should be used. Using a fork-lift can lead to a reduction in back injuries, but watch out – dangerous fork-lift use results in thousands of accidents every year. The main causes of fork-lift accidents are:

- poor training
- dangerous reversing
- driving too quickly
- overloading
- disorganized and crowded work areas
- improper maintenance.

When you make the switch from manual lifting to fork-lifts, proper training of warehouse staff in the best practices should result in an improvement in workplace safety.

**3** Match the words to their meanings.

1 proximity
2 edge
3 detection
4 GPS receiver
5 wireless communications equipment
6 hazard
7 blind spot

a  a danger or risk
b  an area that somebody cannot see
c  a device that uses radio signals to send messages
d  the state of being near to something
e  the act of noticing or discovering something
f  the place where something, especially a surface, ends
g  a piece of equipment that receives signals from the global positioning system, which shows the position of a person or thing on the earth very accurately

**4** Read the text. Then match the sentence halves at the top of page 33.

## Giant dumpers don't have little accidents

It's as big as a house, but it has only a few small windows. How can a vehicle like that be driven safely when there are other vehicles – and people – working nearby?

Accidents involving large vehicles are a big problem in mining, where these big machines are used every day. And even a 'small bump' from one of these monsters can result in terrible damage.

To help prevent accidents, vehicles are fitted with a proximity warning and edge detection system. The system uses wireless communications equipment, computers, and GPS receivers to tell drivers what's going on around them and to warn them when they get too close to a hazard. Proximity warnings are for people and other vehicles, and edge warnings for holes or drops by the side of the road.

How does it work? All of the vehicles on the site are equipped with a GPS receiver and a radio. As they work and move, their location is constantly monitored by a computer. When the system shows that the large vehicle is in danger of hitting another vehicle or a person, the proximity alarm sounds and the driver stops the vehicle immediately. One difficulty with the system is that it can't detect vehicles or people who aren't carrying the correct equipment, so if someone is in the wrong place, accidents still may occur.

The picture shows the driver's blind spots in grey.

1  Small windows in large vehicles
   can result in
2  A minor incident involving a large
   vehicle
3  Accidents can be caused
4  Use of detection equipment
5  Some accidents are due to
6  An edge detection warning can
   result from

a  can lead to improved safety.
b  very poor visibility.
c  vehicles or people not carrying the safety
   equipment.
d  a vehicle driving too near to a hole.
e  can cause a lot of damage.
f  by other vehicles being in a blind spot.

**5**  Read the accident report. Answer the questions.

**ACCIDENT REPORT**

*Date, Time, & Location of Accident:*
27 Mar, 10:35 am, Zone 17, dumping bay 49

*Witness:*
Martin Mobberly, Loader Driver 56004

*Description:*
Maintenance Truck 417 (Kurt Wigan, Mechanic 20050) was waiting in bay 49 for Dumper 673 to arrive so
he could repair its air-conditioning unit. While he was waiting, Wigan telephoned his office to say that he
was having problems with his GPS and radio (signal strength too weak to transmit or receive).
Dumper 568 (Derek Jenkins, Driver 60049) had been cleared to dumping bay 45 but had misunderstood
the message as clearance to bay 49. When Dumper 568 began backing into bay 49, Wigan tried to radio
the truck to stop but remembered that his radio was not working. Wigan left the area immediately and
Dumper 568 backed over and destroyed Maintenance Truck 417. There were no injuries.

1  Where did the accident take place?
   *Zone 17, dumping bay 49*

2  Why was Kurt Wigan in bay 49?

3  What pieces of equipment had insufficient signal power to operate?

4  Who understood an instruction improperly?

5  Which vehicle was in the incorrect dumping bay?

6  When did Wigan try to use his radio?

7  How was Maintenance Truck 417 destroyed?

8  Who was injured in the accident?

9  Why didn't the proximity warning equipment prevent the accident?

**6** Complete the sentences using the words in the list.

> followed   lost   paid attention   paying attention   slipped   talked   tightened
> ~~was slipping~~   was talking   was tightening   were following   was losing

1  The fan belt ..........*was slipping*.......... badly until we ...........................it.

2  He .......................................a bolt on the roof when he .......................................and fell off.

3  She .......................................on her phone and wasn't .......................................to driving.

4  After meeting for an hour in the office, we .......................................for another hour in the café.

5  We .......................................to her instructions and .......................................them very carefully.

6  We .......................................Alistair through the factory, but we .......................................our way in the warehouses.

7  It .......................................a lot of fluid and we couldn't figure out why until we discovered there was a leak.

**7** Complete the crossword.

**Across**

1  Improper maintenance of electrical equipment can lead to electrical ........................... .

4  Road ........................... and other markings need to be very clear to be safe.

7  A ........................... that is difficult to see can cause people to fall over.

8  Workers should be ........................... to carry things safely.

10  Drivers should never ........................... on the phone while driving.

12  Remote ........................... for cranes and other equipment need to be user friendly.

14  People and fork-lift drivers need to be very careful at corner........................... in warehouses.

**Down**

2  Lack of visibility in doorways can cause people to be ........................... over.

3  ........................... doors should never be propped open.

5  Employers must take health and ........................... very seriously.

6  Carrying heavy loads can cause back ........................... .

9  Improper use of gas equipment can cause an ........................... .

11  If you need to reach something in a high place, you should use a proper ........................... .

13  Cables on the floor can cause people to ........................... .

# Unit 9

**1** Look at the pictures. Can you guess what materials these things are made from? Match each picture to a text below. Were your guesses right?

## It's made of what?

1 This is translucent and impervious to rain, but I don't think you'd ever want to wear it – it would probably hurt your head because it's made of glass. ...*g*...

2 You might like to wear this. It's made of 100% recycled plastic from old drinks bottles – thirty of them, to be exact, shredded and made into fabric. ........

3 This is made mostly of wood and it's as strong as a more usual two-wheeler, but more flexible. ........

4 Everyone has heard one of these, but have you ever heard one that's made of steel? It's louder than the usual model and has a sharper sound. ........

5 This vehicle is made of concrete. It's certainly unique, but because it's dense, heavy, and relatively brittle, it's unlikely to become popular. ........

6 Do you recognize this man? Well, he's not a real man, but a copy – made of wax. It's a good material for making models because when it's hot, it's pliable, but when it cools down, it becomes solid. ........

7 This is very comfortable for sitting in. It's made of cardboard, which is very porous. It's light to move around, but it's strong enough to hold the weight of an adult. ........

**2** Read the text. Then answer the questions.

# You could use it for ...

### 1 You could use a seatbelt for ...

repairing a jet engine. A photograph circulating on the internet shows a jet engine with a seatbelt on it. The story behind the photograph is that airline service personnel used the seatbelt to repair the engine and that the plane was flown with this repair in place.

However, the story of the repair is almost certainly untrue. While the photo does show an engine with a belt on it, it is more likely that the engine is being inspected after an accident and the huge fan has been belted in place to stop it from spinning.

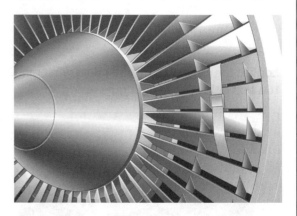

### 2 With a cable tie, we would ...

at least be able to get home. Cable ties are thin bits of plastic designed to hold electrical cables in place; however, they are fantastic for doing all kinds of emergency repairs. Cyclists and campers often carry them because they are so useful in emergency situations where broken equipment can cause real problems.

### 3 A repair with duct tape would ...

last for a few days. Also called duck tape, this cloth tape is another favourite for anyone who needs to make emergency repairs in a hurry. It has many unexpected uses. For example, you could use it to hold your car together after a minor accident.

1 Which picture doesn't actually show a repair? ..1...

2 What material is duct tape made of? ........................

3 Which item used to make a repair is made of plastic? ........................

4 Which of the actual repairs pictured above would probably last longer? ........................

5 What quality do all three of the repair materials share?

    a flexible     b impact-absorbing     c translucent

6 Which two items used to make a repair are made of cloth? ........................ ........................

**3** Match each description of an invention with a picture.

1 If you want to get out of bed at a certain time, it will wake you up with a loud ringing sound. ....*a*....

2 If you need to travel by several means, it will get you there. You can ride it, then fold it up to go in a taxi or a train, then unfold it again and continue riding. ........

3 If you needed to talk to people or have a meeting, you could step inside it. It would 'beam' you to a different location almost instantly. No more jet lag! ........

4 If you need to get somewhere in the city quickly, it's the best way. It's much quicker than a car when traffic is heavy, and it doesn't pollute. ........

5 It's great because it's easy to carry with you and it's very quiet. You can use it to wake you up on a train or plane. ........

6 If you need to talk to someone, you just have to press a few buttons. You can hear their voice very clearly. ........

7 If you wanted to get out of bed at a certain time, it would gently shake your bed until you woke up. If you didn't wake up, it would shake the bed harder and harder, until you fell out. ........

8 If you need to talk to a few people, it'll host a conference with up to five people. It's great because you can see their faces. ........

9 If you needed to ride to the station and get on a train, it would 'deflate' to fit in your brief case. If it were going to work, the material would have to be 'adjustable' on a molecular level. ........

**4** Read the descriptions in **3** again. Which inventions already exist? How does the grammar of the sentences tell you this? Use the words in the list to complete the sentences.

> could   Present Simple   can   Past Simple

If it's in the ...................................¹ tense and uses ...................................² or *will*, it already exists.

If it's in the ...................................³ tense and uses *would* or ...................................⁴, it's imaginary.

**5** Use the words in the list to complete the conversation about one of the inventions on page 37.

> bicycle   built-in   filter   gave up   phone box   scary
> transporting   what if   work   ~~working~~

A What are you ............*working*............[1] on at the moment?

B It's a system for transporting people and things across long distances.

A It looks like a .................................[2].

B Yes, well, it isn't. Step inside. There's no phone in there!

A Er, not just yet. How does it .................................[3]?

B It has .................................[4] sensors. If you stepped inside, they'd read and copy every cell in your body, then re-make you in a different location.

A That sounds .................................[5]!

B Maybe. But also very useful.

A Yes, but .................................[6] there's something else in there with you? Did you see that movie *The Fly*?

B No, I .................................[7] going to the movies a long time ago. Anyhow, there's going to be an air cleaning system. If there's anything in there that shouldn't be, the .................................[8] will catch it.

A Well, I have a better idea for .................................[9] people and things.

B Oh, really?

A Yes. It's called a .................................[10].

**6** Unscramble the sentences about future possibilities.

1 harder / if / worked / would / I / get / promotion / a / I
........................*If I worked harder, I would get a promotion.*........................

2 company / my / if / it / save / would / money / outsourced
If.................................................................................................

3 books / if / had / I / free / time / read / I'd
If.................................................................................................

4 have / too / car / if / bought / I / a / I'd / buy / to / petrol
If.................................................................................................

5 my / wouldn't / if / lot / I / a / of / money / I / job / quit / won
If.................................................................................................

**7** Complete the sentences about your own future possibilities.

1 If I knew how to …
2 If I had a million dollars …
3 If I were my boss …
4 If I could have any job …
5 If I could live anywhere …

# Unit 10

**1** Use the correct form of the verbs in the list to complete the texts.

cook  carve  ~~rotate~~  draw  plan  saw  burn  vibrate

---

## Power tools in the kitchen

*Sawing vegetables safely*

### Vegetable saw

This vegetable saw may look dangerous, but it's really safe.
Instead of ........*rotating*........[1], the blade .........................[2] through
vegetables by .........................[3] very quickly.

*Heating the top of the crème brulée*

### Blow torch

Crème brulée is a popular dessert in Europe. After
.........................[4] it, the chef puts sugar on top and burns it with
a blow torch. It takes practice to heat it until it is crunchy without
.........................[5] it or setting fire to it.

*Carving ice with a saw*

### Chainsaw

In the kitchen? Yes! It's used for carving ice into delicate
shapes to make the table beautiful. The chef will begin by
.........................[6] pictures on paper of the shape he wants to carve.
Before.........................[7] the ice, he will make some marks on it
where he.........................[8] to cut. He will finish the carving by
using smaller hand tools to add details.

---

**2** Match the halves to make true sentences.

1 The vegetable saw cuts     a   instead of setting fire to it.
2 Most circular saws cut     b   before finishing the carving with hand tools.
3 The top of crème brulée is made     c   by vibrating instead of rotating.
4 The chef should heat the sugar carefully     d   after planning the cuts carefully.
5 The chef begins to carve the ice     e   by rotating rather than vibrating.
6 He uses the chainsaw     f   by heating the sugar.

**3** Number the cooking tips in order.

**Cooking rice that doesn't stick together**

a ........ Instead of cooking it right away, let the washed rice sit for fifteen minutes.

b ........ While cooking, you can make the rice less sticky by adding a few drops of lemon juice.

c ...1... You should never cook rice without removing the starch. Here are the steps you should follow.

d ........ Before cooking the rice, wash it until the water runs clear.

e ........ After washing, pour away all of the water.

**Getting rid of cooking smells**

f ........ Begin by putting some sugar in a pan.

g ........ Get rid of a cooking smell in your kitchen by cooking some sugar in a pan. Here's how.

h ........ Instead of smelling of cooking, your kitchen will smell naturally sweet.

i ........ Heat the sugar without burning it.

j ........ After turning light brown, the sugar will begin to smell good.

**4** You are having a conversation with visiting co-workers. For each sentence, tick (✓) appropriate (A) or not appropriate (NA).

| | A | NA | | A | NA |
|---|---|---|---|---|---|
| 1 We've been having really strange weather lately. | ✓ | | 7 You worked with Bev Jensen in London, right? | | |
| 2 Do you go to church? | | | 8 I'll be 50 next year. What about you? | | |
| 3 What do you think of the government? | | | 9 I go swimming every morning before work. | | |
| 4 Do you follow football? | | | 10 What sort of food would you like to eat tonight? | | |
| 5 I got a raise last month. I earn £35,000 a year now. | | | 11 We moved into these offices last year. | | |
| 6 I had a stomach problem last month and went to hospital. | | | 12 Do you have children? | | |

**5** Complete the sentences with the correct form of *used to, be used to,* or *get used to.*

1 Did you ............use to............. work in the Dubai office?

2 Have the guys on the factory floor ................................. the new equipment?

3 I'm not ................................. my new laptop yet, so I keep deleting files accidentally.

4 While we're ................................. our new machines, we're not trying to produce at full capacity.

5 I ................................. go to the gym every day, but I just don't have time now.

6 I didn't ................................. work from home on Thursdays, but now I do.

7 The controls are complicated, but you ................................. them after a while.

8 Mitch says that every time he ................................. his schedule, the management changes it.

9 We ................................. have a factory in Itami City, but we closed it last year.

10 Now that Simon is ................................. getting up at 5:00 every morning, he says it's easy.

**6** **Choose the best response to each sentence.**

1 I heard Bob Cline has left us.
   a Yes, I'm afraid he went to work for the competition.
   b Yes.
   c Yes, that's what he's going to do.

2 Where are you from? Germany?
   a No.
   b Yes, that's right. I live in Munich.
   c Yes, I do. I've worked there for ten years.

3 My wife and kids are coming to join me next week.
   a Oh, great. Do you have any children?
   b Oh, did they? That sounds like fun.
   c Oh, that's nice. What are you going to do?

4 You have a really nice office.
   a Thanks. I really like working here.
   b Yes, I know.
   c I got this when they raised my pay to £75,000.

5 Did you see *The Matrix*?
   a I hate that kind of movie.
   b No, I didn't. Was it any good?
   c No.

6 Did you use to work with Nils Lundstrom in Athens?
   a Yeah, it was OK.
   b Yes, we worked together for about a year.
   c Yes, but I didn't like him very much.

7 What's the weather like in Tokyo?
   a It really depends on the season.
   b Why don't you go there and find out?
   c Not when I was there, but maybe it is now.

8 My car wouldn't start this morning.
   a You should get a better car.
   b Oh.
   c Oh, really? What was wrong with it?

9 Did you see the match last night?
   a No, I don't follow football.
   b No, I didn't.
   c No, I'm not planning to.

10 Do you ever work from home?
   a Yes, I did. I was really good.
   b Yes, OK. Sounds like a good idea.
   c Yes, about twice a month.

**7** Put Sam's lines in the correct place in the conversation.

a Bye!
b ~~Good to see you too, Jim. How you doing?~~
c Oh, no! Is he going to be OK?
d Oh, that's a pity. Why not?
e Really? That's amazing. So what's the delay?
f That must be difficult for you.
g That's a nuisance. Why have they changed it?
h That's excellent news. Are you going to Al Morecomb's presentation this afternoon?
i Well, congratulations.
j Yes, I can imagine. But what about the deal with NVB?

JIM   Hi, Sam. Good to see you!

SAM   ...*b*...¹

JIM   I'm OK, thanks. Hey, have you heard the news? Mark is going to be off work for quite a few weeks. He was badly injured in a car crash yesterday.

SAM   .........²

JIM   Yes, he's going to be OK, but he'll be off work for a while. Oh, I almost forgot to tell you: I'm afraid I can't make it to the conference dinner tonight.

SAM   .........³

JIM   My son and his wife have just had a baby, and we're flying out to see them. I'm a grandfather now!

SAM   .........⁴

JIM   Thanks. I'm happy about that but not so happy that the deal with Harper Robotics fell through. I feel so frustrated to see that all our time and effort were wasted.

SAM   .........⁵

JIM   Oh, that's going great. It looks like we'll finish on time and on budget.

SAM   .........⁶

JIM   Oh, haven't you heard? There was a schedule change. He's speaking tomorrow, not this afternoon.

SAM   .........⁷

JIM   Well, he got a phone call from the lab. They just got some results that show his new material is about 100 times stronger than they thought it was.

SAM   .........⁸

JIM   He needs to re-write the presentation to include the new results. Hey, listen, I've got to go. The elevator's out of service in my hotel, and I'm on the seventh floor.

SAM   .........⁹

JIM   Not really. I need the exercise! See you!

SAM   .........¹⁰

# Unit 11

**1** For each prediction, tick (✓) the certainty the speaker feels.

| Prediction | Certainty the speaker feels | | | | | |
| --- | --- | --- | --- | --- | --- | --- |
| | *100% =*<br>*Certain it will*<br>*happen* | | *50%* | | | *0% =*<br>*Certain it won't*<br>*happen* |
| | a | b | c | d | e | f |
| 1  We almost certainly won't 'grow' human limbs in the next ten years. | | | | | ✓ | |
| 2  We will carry on using organs from human donors for at least the next twenty years. | | | | | | |
| 3  Metamaterials won't completely replace traditional materials immediately. | | | | | | |
| 4  Computer scientists could make a breakthrough in artificial intelligence in the next five years. | | | | | | |
| 5  Astronauts probably won't find evidence of alien life on Mars. | | | | | | |
| 6  A computer will almost certainly pass the Turing Test and converse as well as a human being in the next ten years. | | | | | | |
| 7  The average person isn't likely to have a flying car in the next twenty years. | | | | | | |
| 8  Nanotechnology is likely to solve a lot of problems we now have. | | | | | | |
| 9  There may not be a manned mission to Mars until after 2025. | | | | | | |
| 10  We will probably use a lot more environmentally friendly energy in the near future. | | | | | | |
| 11  Researchers might become expert at 'planting' false memories in the next twenty years. | | | | | | |
| 12  Aliens might not ever visit earth. | | | | | | |

**2** Find words in **1** that mean ...

1  very skilled at – e*xpert*..............
2  find a solution to – s........................
3  have a conversation – c........................
4  space travellers – a........................
5  life from a place other than earth – a........................ ........................
6  created by people, not natural  – a........................

7  normally used, usual – t........................
8  an arm or leg – l............................
9  normal, typical – a........................
10  continue – c........................ ........................
11  not causing harm to the natural world – e........................ ........................
12  carrying a human crew – m........................

**3** Read some predictions from the past. Match each of the three pictures to a prediction.

| | Year | Prediction |
|---|---|---|
| a | 1876 | This 'telephone' has too many shortcomings to be seriously considered as a means of communication. |
| b | 1880s | One day there will be a telephone in every American city. |
| c | 1900 | Persons and things of all kinds will be brought within focus of cameras connected electronically with screens at the opposite ends of circuits, thousands of miles apart. |
| d | 1926 | While theoretically and technically television may be feasible, commercially and financially it is an impossibility. |
| e | 1932 | There is not the slightest indication that nuclear energy will ever be obtainable. It would mean that the atom would have to be shattered at will. |
| f | 1933 | There will never be a bigger plane built. |
| g | 1949 | Computers in the future may have only 1,000 vacuum tubes and weigh only 1.5 tons. |
| h | 1956 | Space travel is complete nonsense. |
| i | 1968 | With over 50 foreign cars already on sale here, the Japanese auto industry isn't likely to carve out a big slice of the U.S. market. |
| j | 1977 | There is no reason anyone would want a computer in their home. |

**4** Can you guess who made each prediction in **3**?

1 ...*j*.... Ken Olson, president, chairman and founder of Digital Equipment Corp.
2 ......... Dr Richard van der Riet Woolley, Astronomer Royal and space adviser to the British government
3 ......... A Boeing engineer, after the first flight of the 247, a twin-engine plane that holds ten people
4 ......... Western Union Telegraph Company internal memo
5 ......... *Popular Mechanics* magazine
6 ......... Albert Einstein
7 ......... Alexander Graham Bell, inventor of the telephone
8 ......... Lee DeForest, inventor and radio pioneer
9 ......... *Ladies Home Journal* magazine
10 ......... *Business Week* magazine

**5** Answer the questions about the predictions in **3**.

1 Which prediction was the most accurate? ...ç...
2 Which other prediction came true? In what way was it a little inaccurate? ........
3 Which prediction is about power generation? ........
4 Yuri Gagarin orbited the earth in 1961. Which prediction did this prove wrong? ........
5 Which prediction didn't imagine the development of microchips? ........
6 What two forms of transportation became a lot more popular than predicted? ........ ........
7 Which invention is described as technically possible but not feasible as a business? ........
8 Who failed to appreciate the importance of the personal computer? ........
9 Which prediction says that an invention has a lot of technical problems? ........

**6** Complete the conversation by writing *can*, *should*, *'ll*, or *'d*.

A What's wrong with it?
B It's really bad. The chain is broken.
A ............*Can*............¹ we repair it?
B No way.
A How much water do we have?
B About six litres – so about three litres each.
A Well, we ................................² wait here and hope someone finds us, or we
................................³ walk.
B I think we ................................⁴ walk. If we continue in this direction,
we ................................⁵ come to a town in 25 kilometres.
A But we'd get tired very quickly walking in this heat. It ................................⁶ be
exhausting. We need to stay with the bike. We can set up the tent here. When we
don't arrive, they ................................⁷ send a search party to look for us.
B Well, I guess so.
A They always say that you ................................⁸ stay with your vehicle.
B Yes, OK, you're right. So we ................................⁹ need to get organized. I ................................¹⁰
see if I can find some firewood and you ................................¹¹ set up the tent.

**7** Complete the crossword.

**Across**

1 Going separate ways is a ............................ idea. We really should stay together.

6 It's best to ............................ as much energy as possible.

8 We have plenty of food, but we may be ............................ later, so we should eat it very carefully.

12 A ............................ is useful if you're walking, so you know which way you're going.

14 We'll become ............................ if we try to walk through the deep snow.

16 I haven't had a shower for days, so I'm ............................ .

17 If we stay near the ............................ , our chances of survival are very good.

18 With the wind and snow, it will be ............................ outside tonight, so wrap up warmly.

19 Joe is ............................ with Sam for forgetting to pack the first aid kit.

20 A large knife is ............................ useful.

**Down**

2 We've got an ............................ bar of chocolate, so that will give us energy for a couple of days.

3 People can ............................ for two days or more at temperatures of 50 °C with no water.

4 The temperature is ............................ during the day, so we should stay in the shade and try to keep cool.

5 You can signal with a cosmetic ............................ .

7 Our chances of survival are ............................ if we make good decisions.

9 Staying with your vehicle is the best ............................ in nearly every case.

10 It was just a ............................ dust cloud at first, but then we realized a car was coming!

11 We can use the empty cigarette lighter to make a ............................ .

13 ............................ foil is useful to make a dry surface to build the fire on.

15 We could use the blanket to make a ............................ .

# Unit 12

1 **Read the conversation between a product user and the help desk at Alarmight. Choose the best help desk response to each thing the caller says.**

*The caller dials and the phone rings.*

ALARMIGHT[1]  a  Hello?
                            b  <u>Good morning. Alarmight. Jane speaking. How can I help?</u>
                            c  Hi, Alarmight here.

CALLER  I'm having problems trying to install the Alarmight A4 home security system. The alarm code doesn't seem to work.

ALARMIGHT[2]  a  OK. Give me your alarm reference number.
                            b  I'm sorry to hear that. Can I have the alarm reference number from the card that came in the box?
                            c  So let me guess: you can't stop the alarm from ringing. OK. What's your alarm reference number?

CALLER  OK. Let's see. It's A4, space, 500 …

ALARMIGHT[3]  a  A4, space, 500 …
                            b  Sorry, I don't need the spaces. Could you start again?
                            c  … and then what?

CALLER  Er, sorry, OK, let's see. It's A4, 500, 2367.

ALARMIGHT[4]  a  So what's the problem?
                            b  You said the alarm is broken?
                            c  And the alarm code isn't working?

CALLER  The alarm code isn't working at all. So I can't set the alarm, and of course if it goes off, I won't be able to turn it off.

ALARMIGHT[5]  a  Yes, I'm afraid the instruction manual isn't as clear as it should be. Have you tried pressing the star key before you enter the code?
                            b  Why don't you just follow the instructions? It's all in the book. It says you need to press the star key before you enter the code.
                            c  Did you use the star key?

CALLER  The star key?

ALARMIGHT[6]  a  Yes. It's on the number pad, at the lower right.
                            b  Yes, the star key.
                            c  No, the moon key, heh heh. Yes, sorry. Er, the star key. It's on the number pad, at the lower right.

CALLER  Just a minute, let me take a look. Oh, yes, I see. Ha. I feel a bit silly for missing that.

ALARMIGHT[7]  a  Yes, most people who call us haven't bothered to read the documentation.
                            b  Don't worry about it. I'd get pretty bored here if the phone never rang!
                            c  Not at all. We're here to help! Don't hesitate to call back if we can help you again.

**2** Look at the order, the invoice, and the pictures of the items that were received. Use the words to make polite complaints.

```
Order
PO number 09909

3 rolls of E430 wire
4 box dust masks
5 pairs safety goggles
1 box 4009 filters
1 wire brush
```

```
Invoice
PO number 07709

4 rolls of E430 wire    €56.44
4 box dust masks        €12.00
5 pairs safety goggles  €20.00
1 box 4009 filters      €48.48
1 wire brush            €1.99
```

1 appear / charge for / wire
    *We appear to have been charged for four rolls of wire.*

2 don't seem / receive / wire

    ...........................................................................

3 looks like / you send / only / dust masks

    ...........................................................................

4 might be / too many / pairs of safety goggles

    ...........................................................................

5 seem / use / PO number

    ...........................................................................

6 looks as if / put in / wrong kind / filters

    ...........................................................................

7 not appear / be / wire brush

    ...........................................................................

**3** Put the apologies in order. Then match each one with a sentence in **2**.

a an / order. / Sorry, / extra / next / we'll / your / send / on / roll
        *Sorry, we'll send an extra roll on your next order.* ......2....

b We'll / away / exchange / them / correct / for / ones / the / right

    ...........................................................................    ........

c tomorrow. / more / you / send / I'll / two / boxes

    ...........................................................................    ........

d away. / right / a / sort / We'll / out / credit

    ...........................................................................    ........

e My / I'll / mistake! / send / invoice. / you / a / new

    ...........................................................................    ........

f sorry / one / I'm / to / about / your / that. / next / I'll / add / order.

    ...........................................................................    ........

g extra / will / tomorrow. / The / ones / driver / the / collect

    ...........................................................................    ........

**4** Match each picture to a description.

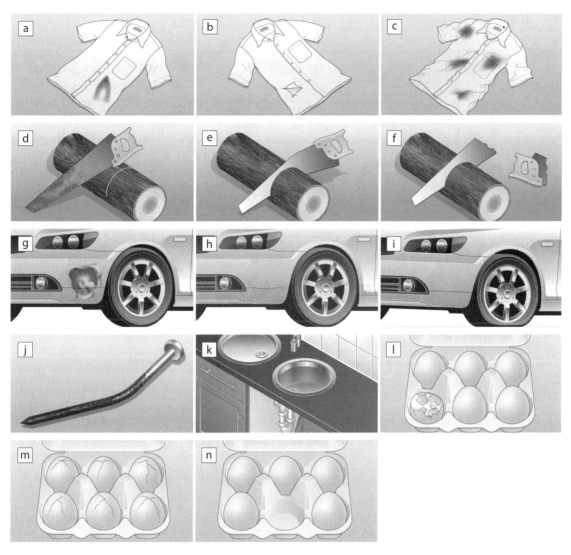

1  ..*d*..  I left it outside and it went rusty and blunt.

2  .........  It's completely blocked. I think it's clogged with grease.

3  .........  They got a bit cracked, but we can still eat them.

4  .........  It got dirty when we took it camping last weekend. The roads were really muddy.

5  .........  I sent it out for cleaning and ironing, and it got scorched and creased.

6  .........  I took it off when I was repairing the car, but it got stained and crumpled.

7  .........  I was cutting the log, but it jammed and broke.

8  .........  I caught it on a nail and it got torn.

9  .........  I was cutting the log, but it jammed and got bent.

10  .........  It got dented when I had a minor accident, and now it's rusty.

11  .........  It's rusted and bent.

12  .........  We ran over a nail and it went flat.

13  .........  It got squashed by the other shopping.

14  .........  There were six, but one got lost.

**5** Use the words in the list to complete the note.

> want  gone  ~~get~~  gets  went  go  getting  goes  got  could

Thanks for looking after the garden while we're away! Here are a few notes:

- The weather is hot, so please water every day. If you don't, some of the plants will ..........._get_.......... ¹ scorched.

- Be careful with the hose. It ..........................² bent and twisted really easily.

- Oh, and there's some fruit in the fridge. Please take it, or it will ..........................³ mouldy.

- After you do the weeding, please put the tools away before you water. They all ..........................⁴ rusty last year after our son let them get wet!

- Can you try to trim the ivy? It's ..........................⁵ tangled in the other plants. I'm afraid it could kill them!

- If you have time, replace the batteries in the torch in the shed. They've ..........................⁶ flat, and you might need it for catching snails and slugs!

- The cat ..........................⁷ missing every day all day, but don't worry – she comes back at night for food.

- Be careful with the lawnmower! It ..........................⁸ jammed last time I used it. I ran over some big sticks. I think I fixed it, but you never know.

- If you ..........................⁹ to invite a few people over for a party in the garden on Saturday night, that's OK! You ..........................¹⁰ use the barbecue to make some food, if you'd like to.

Thanks again for taking care of things. We'll see you in a couple of weeks!

Stan and Linda

**6** Read the text in **5** and match the sentence halves.

1  If the weather is hot,                a  could still be broken.
2  If you aren't careful with the hose,     b  could kill the other plants.
3  The ivy                           c  the plants could get scorched.
4  If you want to catch snails and slugs,   d  it could get bent or twisted.
5  The lawnmower                  e  could use the barbecue.
6  If you want to have a party, you     f  the torch could be useful.

# Unit 13

**1** Read about the progress of several jobs and complete the questions using a passive form.

We've moved the cars and Wilf is digging the trench.

1  What's ............being done............ now?

2  What's already .........................?

We can't bring in the crane until the cables have been removed. And we can't remove the cables until the power is turned off!

3  What can't be done until the cables

.........................?

4  What has to happen before the cables

.........................?

We should be able to finish the roof by the end of the week. And the solar panels will be installed by the end of the month.

5  What should .........................by the end of the week?

6  What should .........................by the end of the month?

We connected the new pipes yesterday but we haven't turned on the water supply yet.

7  Have the new pipes .........................?

8  Has the water supply .........................?

**2** Now answer the eight questions you wrote in **1**. Use passive constructions.

1  ...............*The trench is being dug.*...............

2  .................................................

3  .................................................

4  .................................................

5  .................................................

6  .................................................

7  .................................................

8  .................................................

**3** Look at the words related to volunteering. For each one, tick (✓) the box(es) for the correct category.

| | **a** a person | **b** a personal quality | **c** a skill | **d** a job | **e** a place to work |
|---|---|---|---|---|---|
| 1 a biologist | ✓ | | | ✓ | |
| 2 a chemist | | | | | |
| 3 communication | | | | | |
| 4 computer networking | | | | | |
| 5 converting vehicles | | | | | |
| 6 creative | | | | | |
| 7 detail-oriented | | | | | |
| 8 a disabled motorist | | | | | |
| 9 doing environmental research | | | | | |
| 10 an engineer | | | | | |
| 11 a home for senior citizens | | | | | |
| 12 inventive | | | | | |
| 13 a logistician | | | | | |
| 14 managing inventory | | | | | |
| 15 a member of a global team | | | | | |
| 16 metal work | | | | | |
| 17 a meteorologist | | | | | |
| 18 organizing distribution | | | | | |
| 19 a remote region of the Amazon jungle | | | | | |
| 20 a rural community | | | | | |
| 21 a sailing boat | | | | | |
| 22 a schoolchild | | | | | |
| 23 a scientist | | | | | |
| 24 a senior citizen | | | | | |
| 25 setting up a website | | | | | |
| 26 supervising projects | | | | | |
| 27 teaching children | | | | | |
| 28 training residents | | | | | |
| 29 troubleshooting | | | | | |
| 30 well organized | | | | | |
| 31 woodwork | | | | | |

**4** Use words from **3** to complete the advertisement.

Are you interested in becoming ....._a member of a global team_....[1]? Our volunteers, from all over the world, work in Asia, Africa, and South America ..........................[2] to find out how we can reduce the human impact on the natural world. We need experienced people with a variety of skills and professional abilities:
- A ..........................[3] to help us understand how weather and human activity are related
- A ..........................[4] to work closely with our team's biologist to carry out water and soil analysis
- Someone with experience in ..........................[5] to be responsible for setting up and linking the ten computer stations and central server in our London office

If you don't want to work in ..........................[6] in a faraway country, you could work here in the UK ..........................[7] so that people who use the internet can find out more about our work.

**5** Match the interview questions with the answers.

| | | | |
|---|---|---|---|
| 1 | How long did you work for PVS? | a | I've worked there for three years. |
| 2 | Have you ever been to Peru? | b | I worked there for three years. |
| 3 | How long have you lived in France? | c | Yes, I went there twice. |
| 4 | How long have you studied Spanish? | d | Yes, I've been there twice. |
| 5 | When did you study Spanish? | e | Yes, I lived there for six months. |
| 6 | Did you go to China when you lived in Vietnam? | f | I've lived there since last October. |
| 7 | How long have you worked for AVP? | g | I qualified last year, in July. |
| 8 | Have you ever lived in South America? | h | I've been qualified for six years. |
| 9 | When did you qualify as an accountant? | i | I studied it when I was at university. |
| 10 | How long have you been a qualified pilot? | j | I've studied it for four years now. |

**6** It is now the year 2020. Look at the timeline. Use the words to write true sentences.

| | 2012 | 2013 | 2014 | 2015 | 2016 | 2017 | 2018 | 2019 | 2020 (now) |
|---|---|---|---|---|---|---|---|---|---|
| Work for TTD | ▓ | ▓ | ▓ | ▓ | | | | | |
| Work for AMX | | | | | ▓ | ▓ | ▓ | ▓ | ▓ |
| Live in Newbiggin | ▓ | ▓ | ▓ | ▓ | ▓ | ▓ | | | |
| Live in Arbuckle | | | | | | | ▓ | ▓ | ▓ |
| Study Chinese | | | | ▓ | ▓ | ▓ | ▓ | ▓ | ▓ |

1 work / TTD / four years
............._I worked for TTD for four years._...............

2 work / AMX / five years
..................................................................

3 live / Newbiggin / from / to
..................................................................

4 live / Arbuckle
..................................................................

5 started studying Chinese
..................................................................

6 study Chinese / six years
..................................................................

7 left TTD
..................................................................

8 not study Chinese / before 2015
..................................................................

9 work / TTD / now
..................................................................

10 live / now
..................................................................

**7** Read the postcard. For each sentence below, circle T (true) or F (false).

*27 August*

Dear Pascal,
I arrived in Egypt three days ago, but
I'm still in Cairo! I've been delayed
leaving because of problems with the
Land Rover. It's been repaired, but I'm
being taken care of so well here, I don't
want to leave! (I've been fed wonderful
homemade food every night by Ahmed
and Azira.) Anyhow, the installation at
Al Fayyum still needs to be done, so I'll
have to get back to work soon!
See you soon.
Geno

TO:
28
Paris
FRA

| | | | |
|---|---|---|---|
| 1 Geno has been in Egypt for a week. | T / F | 5 Geno thinks Ahmed and Azira serve good food. | T / F |
| 2 Geno is still in Cairo. | T / F | | |
| 3 The Land Rover isn't working now. | T / F | 6 Geno has already repaired the installation at Al Fayyum. | T / F |
| 4 Geno wants to leave Cairo. | T / F | | |

**8** Use the words in the list to complete the telephone conversation.

> won't   was   should   ~~has~~   can   have   can't   are

KELLY    How's it going?

GENO     We're behind schedule.

KELLY    The installation ..........*has*..........¹ to be finished by Tuesday.

GENO     We lost several days because the Land Rover .........................² being repaired.

KELLY    How .........................³ you getting on?

GENO     Everything was unpacked this morning. The sheet metal press is being assembled today so it .........................⁴ be wired in tomorrow.

KELLY    It .........................⁵ already be finished by now, you know. This job has to be done by Tuesday. The deadline .........................⁶ be extended. The opening has been scheduled for Wednesday, and the machines .........................⁷ to be working.

GENO     Don't worry. It .........................⁸ be a problem.

**9** Answer the questions about the conversation in **8**.

1 What's been done so far? (When?)
   *Everything has been unpacked. It was unpacked this morning.*

2 What's being done now?
   .............................................................................................

3 What hasn't been done yet?
   .............................................................................................

# Unit 14

**1** Complete the puzzle by writing the name of the symbol. Number 12 is the name for all of these marks.

1 '
2 ?
3 ( ) (in US Eng)
4 ,
5 ( ) (in UK Eng)
6 . (in UK Eng)
7 /
8 ABC etc.
9 . (in US Eng)
10 !
11 -

**2** These sentences refer to items 1–11 in **1**. For each sentence, circle T (true) or F (false).

| | | |
|---|---|---|
| 1 | This is used to indicate a slight pause in a sentence. | T / (F) |
| 2 | This shows that a sentence is a question. | T / F |
| 3 | These show that information is missing from a sentence. | T / F |
| 4 | This symbol can be used to separate items in a list. | T / F |
| 5 | These enclose extra information within a sentence. | T / F |
| 6 | This symbol is used to indicate alternatives. | T / F |
| 7 | This symbol is sometimes used in website addresses. | T / F |
| 8 | These are used at the start of a sentence to show strong emotion. | T / F |
| 9 | This symbol is usually used to separate items in a list. | T / F |
| 10 | This can be used to show strong emotion. | T / F |
| 11 | This shows that two words are missing from a list of information. | T / F |

**3** Correct the punctuation error in each of these sentences.

1 Has Ian arrived yet! *Has Ian arrived yet?*

2 Bring your computer equipment (scanner, printer, cables, and so on.

3 We need to order some new chairs for the conference room

4 He forgot to bring the plans his laptop the schedule and his glasses.

5 did you get my message?

6 Which room is the meeting going to be held in.

7 It doesnt matter if we arrive late.

8 We've made 95% on/time deliveries this month.

**4** Match each of these writing problems with a sentence in the text.

a  unnecessary commas ..........2......

b  incorrect apostrophe .........

c  inappropriate abbreviation .........

d  improper capitalization .........

e  colloquialism .........

f  incorrect spelling .........

g  missing word .........

h  incorrect subject-verb agreement .........

i  adverb used instead of adjective .........

j  double negative .........

k  not specific enough .........

l  redundancy .........

---

## Underfloor heating by Heatco

Have you thought about using underfloor heating under and below your floor?[1] At Heatco, we think, you should, think about it. [2] Heatco is much better.[3]

Underfloor heating is a very efective way to heat your home.[4] It allow's you to keep you home cooler because if your feet feel warm, your whole body feels warm.[5] It's as easily to install as conventional heating when a new home is built, and it is no more expensive than conventional heating.[6] It also ain't uncommon to replace an existing conventional heating system with underfloor heating.[7]

Und. fl. htg. works best when a home is well insulated.[8] We recommend upgrading your Insulation when your Underfloor Heating is installed.[9] Our engineers is happy to visit your home to carry out an insulation check and inspection to see if your home is suitable for underfloor heating.[10] We won't make no charge for our initial consultation.[11] We'll your home, let you know if we think it's suitable for underfloor heating, and give you an exact price for installation.[12]

*Call Heatco today!*

---

**5** How should each of these words be written in the text?

1  efective (sentence 4) ..........*effective*..........

2  allow's (sentence 5) .............................

3  easily (sentence 6) .............................

4  ain't (sentence 7) .............................

5  Und. fl. htg. (sentence 8) .............................

6  Underfloor Heating (sentence 9) .............................

7  is (sentence 10) .............................

8  no (sentence 11) .............................

**6** What do the non-metric quantities measure? Tick (✓) the correct box.

| | a weight | b volume | c pressure | d temperature | e length/height |
|---|---|---|---|---|---|
| 1 degrees Fahrenheit | | | | ✓ | |
| 2 foot | | | | | |
| 3 gallon | | | | | |
| 4 inch | | | | | |
| 5 ounce | | | | | |
| 6 pint | | | | | |
| 7 pound | | | | | |
| 8 stone | | | | | |
| 9 yard | | | | | |
| 10 pounds per square inch | | | | | |

**7** Match each metric measurement with its equivalent.

| | | | |
|---|---|---|---|
| 1 | 0 °C | a | 1/10mth of the earth's circumference |
| 2 | 1 dm³ | b | 1 kg |
| 3 | weight of 1 L water | c | 1 dm |
| 4 | 1,000 kg of water | d | 1 mm |
| 5 | 1,000 m | e | 1 m |
| 6 | 1/10 m | f | boiling point of water |
| 7 | 1/100 m | g | 1 cm |
| 8 | 1/1000 m | h | freezing point of water |
| 9 | 10 m | i | 100 dm |
| 10 | 100 °C | j | volume of 1 L water |
| 11 | 1 m | k | 1 t |
| 12 | 10 dm | l | 1 km |

**8** Use one word from each column to make seven calculations and complete the puzzle. There is only one complete / correct solution.

| | | | | | |
|---|---|---|---|---|---|
| 1 | One | ~~minus~~ | ten | makes two. | 1 *Nine minus three is six.* |
| 2 | Three | plus | two | is forty. | 2 ................................................ |
| 3 | Four | times | ~~three~~ | equals five. | 3 ................................................ |
| 4 | Five | divided by | five | leaves seven. | 4 ................................................ |
| 5 | Six | from | eight | ~~is six.~~ | 5 ................................................ |
| 6 | ~~Nine~~ | fives | twelve | equals ten. | 6 ................................................ |
| 7 | Ten | into | are | fifteen. | 7 ................................................ |

**9** Read the text. Match the bold words in the text to the labels on the picture.

### Leonardo da Vinci

In the 1400s, long before the metric system was invented, Leonardo da Vinci wanted to make the connection between measurements and nature. His famous 'Vitruvian Man' drawing shows the connections between various measurements. At da Vinci's time, both cubit and pace were common measurements of length. The notes around the drawing indicate that:

- ❖ a **palm**[1] is the width of four fingers.
- ❖ a **foot**[2] is the width of four palms (about 12 inches).
- ❖ a cubit is the width of six palms.
- ❖ a man's height is four cubits (and thus 24 palms).
- ❖ a pace is four cubits.
- ❖ the length of a man's outspread **arms**[3] is equal to his height.
- ❖ the distance from the **hairline**[4] to the bottom of the **chin**[5] is one tenth of a man's height.
- ❖ the distance from the top of the head to the bottom of the chin is one eighth of a man's height.
- ❖ the maximum width of the **shoulders**[6] is a quarter of a man's height.
- ❖ the distance from the **elbow**[7] to the tip of the hand is one fifth of a man's height.
- ❖ the distance from the elbow to the **armpit**[8] is one eighth of a man's height.
- ❖ the length of the hand is one tenth of a man's height.
- ❖ the distance from the bottom of the chin to the nose is one third of the length of the head.
- ❖ the distance from the hairline to the **eyebrows**[9] is one third of the length of the face.
- ❖ the length of the ear is one third of the length of the face.

a ....................
b ....................
c ....................
d ....................
e ....................
f ....................
g ....................
h ....................
i ....................

**10** Answer these questions. According to the text in **9**, when a man's height is four cubits as in the picture,

1 how many fingers wide is a foot? ............16............

2 what is the width of a man's outspread arms in cubits? ....................

3 how many palms is the distance from the top of a man's head to the bottom of the chin?

....................

4 what's the maximum width of a man's shoulders in cubits? ....................

5 what's the distance from the elbow to the tip of a man's hand in palms? ....................

6 what's the distance from the elbow to the armpit in palms? ....................

7 what's the distance from the hairline to the bottom of the chin (that is, the length of the face) in fingers? ....................

8 how many fingers is the distance from the hairline to the eyebrows? ....................

# Unit 15

**1** Match the descriptions to the site plans.

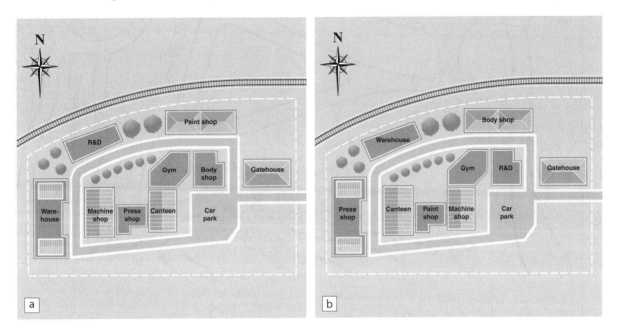

a

b

1 ...*a*... The machine shop is located between the warehouse and the press shop.

2 ......... There's a warehouse opposite the machine shop.

3 ......... The body shop is near the north-east corner of the site.

4 ......... If you're in the car park facing west, the paint shop is behind the machine shop.

5 ......... The body shop, gym, and canteen are all next to the car park.

6 ......... The body shop is opposite R&D.

7 ......... The warehouse is in the south-west corner of the site.

8 ......... The canteen is next to the paint shop.

**2** Complete these sentences about plan a in **1**. Use the words in the list.

in front of   between   R&D   ~~backs onto~~   opposite   boundary

1 R&D ...........*backs onto*........... the railway tracks.

2 The body shop is ................................. the gate house.

3 The warehouse is near ................................. .

4 The road runs ................................. the machine shop and the warehouse.

5 The paint shop is located on the northern ................................. of the site.

6 There's a car park ................................. the canteen.

**3** Follow the directions. Which corner of the map do they take you to?

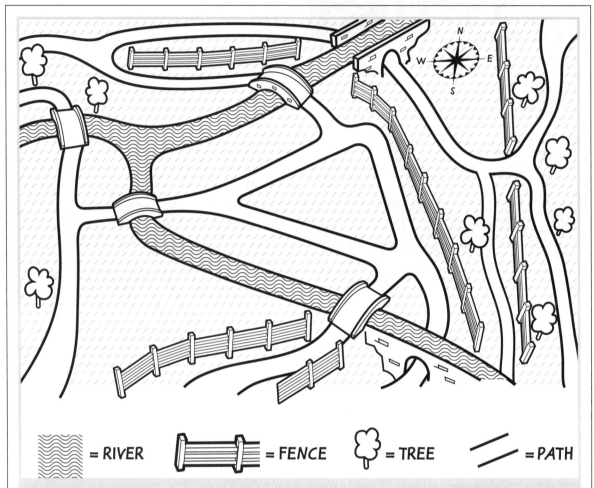

= RIVER    = FENCE    = TREE    = PATH

Begin in the south-west corner of the site. Walk north until you can turn to the right and go over the river. After you cross the river, veer left, walking parallel to the river. Turn left to cross over the river again, and then walk parallel to the fence. At the end of the fence, do a U-turn to walk on the opposite side of the fence. Continue walking east. Pass under the river. Walk south-east and then veer east to walk between two fences. Turn left, walk between two trees, and you're there!

**4** Match the sentence halves.

1 This first part of the          a the railway track.
2 We connected                   b see where it changes direction.
3 It was pretty easy to          c to use acoustic locators.
4 It runs parallel to            d pipe is metal.
5 That's where the job           e radio transmitters to it.
6 The metal pipe becomes a       f got tricky.
7 We had                         g deep in the ground.
8 We found the pipe suddenly     h above it and induce a signal.
9 Under the                      i foundry, it becomes a metal pipe again.
10 It's buried very              j veers north-east.
11 We had to place a coil        k disappeared.
12 The signals                   l concrete pipe at that point.

**5** Use the words in the list to complete the sentences. Then match each sentence with one of the five *Ss* below.

find   maintain   set up   ~~get rid of~~   make

1 Keep the things you need to get jobs done and ..........*get rid of*.......... the rest.
2 Tidy up, apply labels, and make things easy to ................................. and reach.
3 Sweep up and ................................. the place spotless.
4 ................................. routines that make it easy to stay clutter free, orderly, and clean.
5 Monitor your results and ................................. the new system.

a ...4... Standardize
b ......... Sweep and shine
c ......... Sort
d ......... Straighten
e ......... Sustain

**6** Read the text. For each sentence below, circle T (true) or F (false).

## Top tips for efficient email management

Many workers feel that checking, reading, and answering email takes up too much time. How can we keep up with emailing without spending too much time at it? Here are four tips that will help you use email more efficiently.

- Turn off the 'new mail' sound on your email program. You don't need to read every email as soon at it arrives.
- Turn on the features of your email program that will help organize your messages. Most email applications can identify unwanted messages and transfer them directly to the trash so you don't need to waste time reading them.
- Schedule certain times each day that you will deal with email. This will allow you to concentrate on your work. Stick to this routine. You don't need to answer every message immediately!
- Don't use your most productive time of day for emailing. If you do your best work in the morning, don't waste your most creative time with emailing. It will probably take you twice as long, and you won't be fresh and alert for doing your work.

1 A lot of workers feel that email makes them more efficient.                                       T / (F)
2 It saves time if you look at every message when it arrives.                                        T / F
3 Most email software can help you read every message.                                              T / F
4 It saves time if your email program throws away unwanted messages before you
  read them.                                                                                         T / F
5 It's best if you read email only at certain times of day.                                          T / F
6 The only way to keep up with email is to reply to every message when you receive it.              T / F
7 The best time to write email is when you are feeling the most fresh and alert, for
  example first thing in the morning.                                                                T / F

**7** **Unscramble the sentences.**

1  ask / let's / out / it / to / maintenance / check.
   *Let's ask maintenance to check it out.*

2  later / we / boxes / can / those / rid / get / of.
   ...............................................................

3  that / onto / plastic / let's / sheeting / hold.
   ...............................................................

4  the / through / want / to / me / do / tools / you / sort?
   ...............................................................

5  out / figure / is / system / hard / the / to.
   ...............................................................

6  labels / the / off / falling / keep.
   ...............................................................

**8** **Use the words in brackets to make offers of help.**

1  A  The store room is a mess. (tidy up).
   B  I'll ................... *tidy it up.* ...................

2  A  Someone needs to organize these boxes. (take care)
   B  I'll ...............................................................

3  A  There's sand all over the floor. (sweep up)
   B  I'll ...............................................................

4  A  These tools are all mixed up. (sort out)
   B  I'll ...............................................................

5  A  There's a problem with the coffee maker. (sort out)
   B  I'll ...............................................................

6  A  There's a big oil spill in the car park. (clean up)
   B  I'll ...............................................................

**9** **Complete the crossword puzzle. Which of the verbs in the puzzle are separable?**

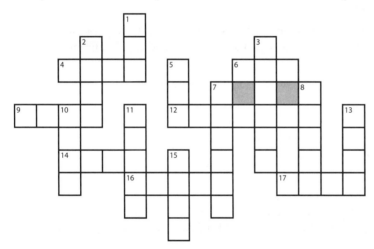

**Across**

4  We need to .........................up with a better system.
6  Where can I get .........................of the empty boxes?
9  Can you help me .........................for the keys to the store room?
12  Sort .........................the tools and find the ones we use every day.
14  I'll .........................care of the recycling.
16  We need to .........................up the kitchen.
17  Put .........................those tools, please.

**Down**

1  I'm going to .........................to that leak this afternoon.
2  Did you .........................out the best way to store the drill?
3  I can't .........................out what's causing the problem.
5  I'm going to .........................on with the tidying while you clean the floors.
7  I'll probably get .........................to repairing the lamp this afternoon.
8  .........................away the roller if we can't repair it.
10  We should hold .........................the spare parts.
11  .........................out the motor.
13  .........................up your workbench, please.
15  .........................up the good work!

# Unit 16

**1** **Use the words and phrases in the list to complete the email.**

> I'm attaching   Is there   It would also be good   Please confirm
> ~~Thanks~~   There will be   Would you like   Can

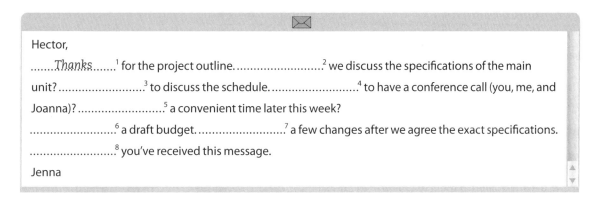

Hector,

........*Thanks*........[1] for the project outline. .........................[2] we discuss the specifications of the main

unit? .........................[3] to discuss the schedule. .........................[4] to have a conference call (you, me, and

Joanna)? .........................[5] a convenient time later this week?

.........................[6] a draft budget. .........................[7] a few changes after we agree the exact specifications.

.........................[8] you've received this message.

Jenna

**2** **Which of these emails**

1  is the least clear? ...*b*....

2  is the least friendly? .........

3  is repetitive? .........

4  is the least professional? .........

5  is professional, clear, concise, and friendly?

.........

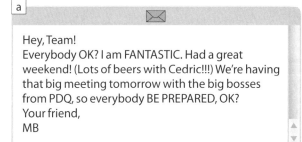

**a**

Hey, Team!
Everybody OK? I am FANTASTIC. Had a great
weekend! (Lots of beers with Cedric!!!) We're having
that big meeting tomorrow with the big bosses
from PDQ, so everybody BE PREPARED, OK?
Your friend,
MB

**b**

Dirk,
Hi! Rgding project, Ian said Mike said you had
taken some steps on improving the ideas we
needed sorting out as soon as we can. OK?
Cheers,
Mitch

**c**

Arno,
If you have the time, could you look into the
schedule of the Williams project, please, and
get back to me? If it's OK with you, could you
check how the schedule looks and let me
know? Are we on schedule, or are we late? Do
this if you have time, please. I just want to know
if we're behind schedule or not. Do you mind?
Blixa

**d**

Ian,
We need to discuss the
schedule for the XB-35.
Would you like to meet when
you're in Bristol next week?
It would also be good to
discuss the budget for the
XB-38.
Charles

**e**

Simone,
You must sort out
the schedule for the
PB-889 immediately.
Gill

**3** Rewrite these sentences so that they are clear and professional.

1 THNQ 4 sending your flight details yesterday.
................*Thank you for sending your flight details yesterday.*................

2 We'd like to see you and meet you to talk with you about the specifications.
....................................................................................................................

3 I'm attaching in the attached file some information for our meeting 2MORO.
....................................................................................................................

4 Let me know if U need more information or if I can send you more information.
....................................................................................................................

5 I'll post a replacement nozzle will be sent to you 2DAY.
....................................................................................................................

**4** Read the article. Label the parts of the disc brake assembly.

# How you make it stop

The brake system on this motorcycle is hydraulic. That means that it works by pushing a type of oil, called brake fluid, through the system to operate the mechanical parts.

Here is a description of the main parts of the brake system:

- At the very top of the system is the **brake fluid reservoir**. This is a small tank that holds the brake fluid, which you pour in by removing the **filler cap**.

- The reservoir is attached to the **master cylinder**. There is a **piston** that moves in and out of the cylinder when the brakes are operated.

- The **brake line** is a narrow tube that attaches to the bottom of the master cylinder. It connects the master cylinder to the **calliper assembly**. This is a mechanical device that opens and closes. When the callipers close, they touch the disc so it rotates more slowly or stops. When they open, the disc rotates freely.

- The **disc** is the circular part at the bottom. It's attached to the wheel of the motorcycle.

So how does it work? When the driver squeezes the brake handle, the **push rod** pushes the piston into the master cylinder. That pushes the brake fluid down the brake line, which pushes the callipers shut. This causes the bike to slow down or stop.

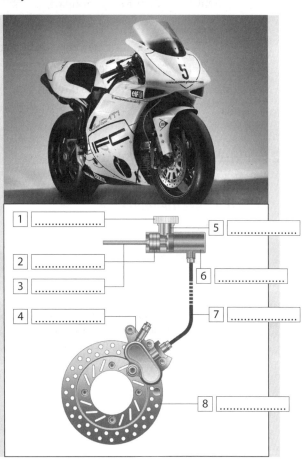

**5** For each sentence below, circle T (true) or F (false).

1 Brake fluid is mainly used to lubricate the mechanical parts.　T /(F)
2 The brake fluid reservoir has a removable cap.　T / F
3 The brake fluid pushes the piston into the master cylinder.　T / F
4 The brake line connects to the disc.　T / F
5 The callipers open and close.　T / F
6 The push rod is connected to the piston in the master cylinder.　T / F

**6** Tick (✓) the column that shows how the part is being identified.

| | a The class it belongs to | b Adjectives | c Components or features | d Locations or connections | e What things do | f Purpose |
|---|---|---|---|---|---|---|
| 1 It's cylindrical. | | ✓ | | | | |
| 2 It's located between part XJ36 and part B8X. | | | | | | |
| 3 It rotates. | | | | | | |
| 4 It's for draining the tank. | | | | | | |
| 5 It's used to monitor the system. | | | | | | |
| 6 It has a plug. | | | | | | |
| 7 It attaches to part B8X. | | | | | | |
| 8 It's a type of chain. | | | | | | |
| 9 It moves in and out. | | | | | | |
| 10 It has a door on one side. | | | | | | |

**7** Match each description in **6** to a part of the device below.

**8** Complete the puzzle.

1 A metal coil that returns to its original shape after being pressed, pushed, or pulled.

2 The flat part of a knife, tool, or machine which has a sharp edge or edges for cutting.

3 A set of wheels with tooth-shaped parts on their edge that interconnect.

4 A device that's wide at the top and narrow at the bottom, used for pouring liquids and powders into a small opening.

5 A long, continuous moving band of rubber, metal, or cloth, used to transport goods from one part of a building to another – conveyor ..........................

6 A glass tube partially filled with liquid which has a bubble of air inside. It's used for checking things are horizontal – ..........................level

7 A small wire or device inside a piece of electrical equipment used to break the current if the flow of electricity is too strong.

8 A plastic or glass tube with a long hollow needle or hollow rubber part at the end that's used for sucking up liquid and then pushing it out.

9 A series of metal rings which are linked together.

10 A curved piece of plastic or glass that makes things appear larger, smaller, or clearer when you look through it.

11 An instrument for measuring the level or amount of something. The level or amount is displayed by a needle and a scale.

12 A device for lifting and lowering objects. It has a wheel or wheels and a length of string or chain.

13 A machine with blades that go round and create a current of air.

14 Cylindrical pieces of wood, metal, or plastic that roll over and over and are used in machines, for example to make something flat.

15 A wheel with a row of teeth around the edge that connect with the holes of a chain or holes in film and so on in order to turn it.

16 An instrument with a needle that always points to the north.

17 What you've been doing to complete this puzzle!

# Unit 17

**1** Look at the pictures. Today is Monday 10 May. Use the words in the list to complete the sentences.

will  ~~broke down~~  will have been  has been  is  had

1  The lift ............*broke down*............ a week ago.
2  The lift ................................ out of action for a week.
3  The lift ................................ out of action now.
4  The lift ................................ out of action for two weeks when they fix it.
5  They ................................ fix it next week.
6  A loose wire ................................ caused a short and damaged the motor.

**2** Read the conversation. For each statement below, circle T (true) or F (false).

A  We have a problem. If we can't ship the brake assemblies to Falcon next Friday, they'll cancel the order.
B  That's going to be difficult. Can't they give us until Monday the 25th?
A  No. They'll have run out of stock by Monday the 25th. And our assembly line is still down.
B  But it broke down a week ago. What's the hold up?
A  We're waiting for a new part. It should be here by tomorrow.
B  So what's the problem?
A  Falcon want 10,000 brake assemblies.
B  Well, we have 2,700 ready to go.
A  Yes, but we'll only have made another 3,000 by next Friday.

1  Falcon haven't cancelled their order.                    Ⓣ/ F
2  It's already later than Monday the 25th.                  T / F
3  The brake assemblies have been delivered to Falcon.       T / F
4  Falcon has already run out of stock.                      T / F
5  The assembly line hasn't been repaired yet.               T / F
6  The assembly line has been broken for about two
   weeks.                                                    T / F
7  The replacement part for the assembly line hasn't yet
   arrived.                                                  T / F
8  They need to make 8,300 more brake assemblies by
   next Friday.                                              T / F

Monday 3 May

Monday 10 May

LIFT OUT OF ORDER

Monday 17 May

**3** Read the story. Number the pictures. But be careful! It isn't easy. You should read the entire story first before you begin numbering.

After I bought my bicycle, I cycled to work every day. It was a wonderful change. I had driven to work for three years before that, and I was really tired of all the traffic. Before I started driving my car to work, I walked. It was nice, but it always took a long time. And after I had walked to work for about a year, I took a skiing holiday. I fell and broke my leg, and I couldn't walk to work any more, so I started driving. After I gave up driving and I had cycled for about a year, my bicycle was stolen. I was really busy at the time and didn't have time to buy a new one, but I didn't want to drive my car to work, either. So I started running to work! That was nearly a year ago. Next week, I will have run to work for a whole year, and so I am going to celebrate. How? I'm going to buy a new pair of running shoes!

**4** Read the sentences. Can you complete the checklist in the correct order?

- *You can't update the budget until you've talked with Liam.*
- *You can visit the Singapore office sometime after you've updated the budget.*
- *You will have had Susan's input before you ask for production's input.*
- *After you've updated the budget, you'll talk with Adam.*
- *You'll have to talk with Adam before you visit the Singapore office.*
- *You will have visited the Singapore office before you prepare the drawings.*
- *You'll need Susan's input after you've prepared the drawings.*
- *After you've done all that, you'll go on holiday!*

Checklist

1 Talk with.............................................

2 ...........................................................

3 Talk with.............................................

4 ...........................................................

5 ...........................................................

6 ...............................................input.

7 ...............................................input.

8 ...........................................................

**5** Circle the picture in each category that doesn't belong.

1 has small parts that may present a choking hazard

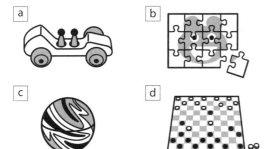

2 may contain lead paint that is toxic if ingested

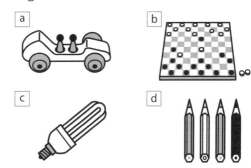

3 could shatter

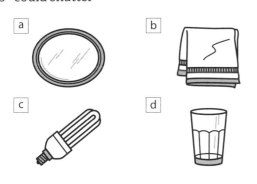

4 may pose a fire hazard

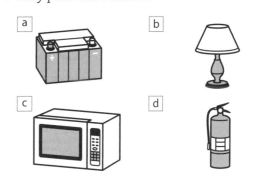

5 may have an intermittent electrical fault

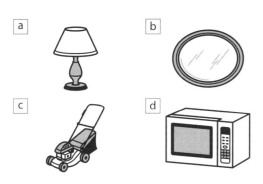

6 might have a short that could scorch the plastic case

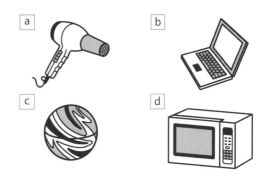

**6** Read the product recall announcement. Which item pictured in **5** is it referring to?

---

**Recall notice: Catalogue Item T-125**

Issued 1 February 2009

We have become aware of a potential problem that may affect our Catalogue Item T-125 manufactured since 15 January 2009.

This product is not up to normal quality standards and could break when filled with very hot or very cold liquids. If you are using this product and think it may have this problem, please stop using it immediately and contact us.

**7** Match the descriptions to the pictures.

1 This might have been caused by an animal. ...ª...
2 That could lead to a fire. .........
3 It might not have been properly installed. .........
4 This might result in delays. .........
5 That could cause someone to fall. .........
6 That may affect the delivery schedule. .........

**8** Match the sentence halves to show the most likely cause-and-effect relationships.

1 The fan made a loud noise and then it stopped working.
2 The brakes aren't working very well now.
3 The cap fell off the petrol tank while we were driving.
4 The motor is really hot.
5 The lift isn't working.
6 One of the four assembly lines is down.
7 What happens if you put the wrong fuel in the fuel tank?
8 We just lost a major customer.

a It can cause the engine to fail.
b That could cause the stairs to be very crowded.
c It might have been caused by a loose screw.
d It might result in the wires melting.
e That could lead to cash-flow problems.
f It might not have been tightened.
g That may affect the number of pieces we can produce by next Friday.
h That could lead to serious problems with stopping the car!

# Unit 18

**1** Read the email. Then match the sentence halves.

---

✉

Hey, Mel.
How are you doing? Did you have a good weekend? I was supposed to go to the beach with Simon and Rachel, but my car broke, so I just stayed at home.
I'm OK, but there's a big problem here at work. You remember my colleague Dan? Well, he was supposed to finish a big presentation for a meeting today. So last Friday, he took an office laptop home for the weekend so he could work on the presentation. But guess what? He went to the pub after work and LOST THE LAPTOP! OH, NO! That's bad, because we're not supposed to take laptops home without permission. But this is worse: It had some VERY SENSITIVE information on it. He shouldn't have taken that information out of the building, and he definitely shouldn't have lost it. He should have gone straight home with the computer and left it there.
I guess Dan will soon be looking for a new job. (He hasn't told our boss yet, but I told him he should do it right away, because it will only get worse the longer he leaves it.)
I should say goodbye now. I'm not supposed to write personal email at work!
Malcolm

---

1 Malcolm had expected
2 Dan was expected
3 Dan should have
4 Dan wasn't supposed
5 Dan shouldn't have
6 Malcolm thinks Dan should
7 Dan should have taken
8 Malcolm isn't supposed

a to prepare a big presentation.
b to take sensitive information out of the building.
c the computer straight home.
d to go to the beach at the weekend.
e asked permission to take a laptop home.
f lost the laptop.
g to write personal email at work.
h tell his boss what's happened.

**2** Look at the activities in the list. Do they relate to the security of a building, computers, or information? Tick (✓) the correct column.

| | a  a building | b  computers | c  information |
|---|---|---|---|
| 1  implementing clean desk policies | | | ✓ |
| 2  classifying information | | | |
| 3  securing access doors | | | |
| 4  installing computer firewalls | | | |
| 5  issuing employee ID cards | | | |
| 6  encrypting email | | | |
| 7  using and regularly changing passwords | | | |
| 8  shredding documents | | | |
| 9  shutting down at the end of the day | | | |

**3** Use the words in the list to complete the rules.

photos  cameras  visitors  guards  security  prototypes  ~~doors~~  phones

......Doors......¹
**should be locked at all times.**

........................² and mobile ........................³ should be handed in to ........................⁴ before entry.

........................⁵ **should be accompanied by security** ........................⁶**.**

........................⁷**should be covered when outside contractors are present.**

**Taking**........................⁸ **inside the lab is not allowed.**

**4** The rules in **3** apply to the lab below. Look at the picture and choose one word or phrase from each column to make five true sentences.

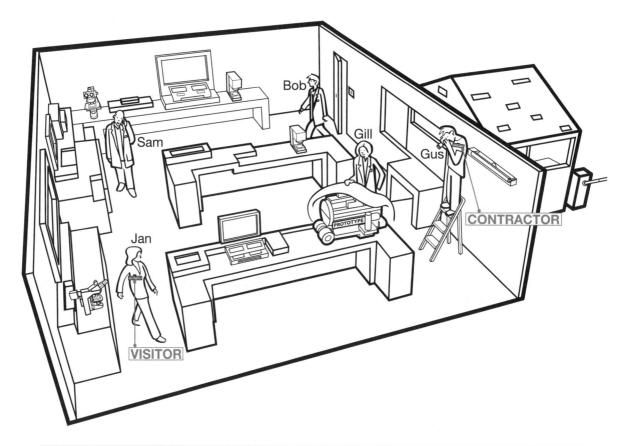

| | | | | |
|---|---|---|---|---|
| 1 | Bob | isn't allowed | accompanied by | the prototype. |
| 2 | Sam | should be | to take | his phone. |
| 3 | Jan | should | uncover | a photograph. |
| 4 | Gill | shouldn't | handed in | a security guard. |
| 5 | Gus | should have | lock | the door. |

**5** Complete the crossword.

**Across**

2  We are very careful with our security, so ........................into the system would be very difficult.

3  Only a few employees have super-user ........................to the system.

6  All sensitive........................on computers must be protected by a password.

7  Our corporate ........................is protected by a firewall.

10  Every year, an outside company does a security ........................of our system to make sure it's still secure.

13  A few years ago, some network ........................ helped us set up our security system.

14  Our ........................is thrown away the usual way, but most paper needs to be shredded.

15  You need a ........................to open the door to the research lab.

**Down**

1  If anyone leaves their computer ........................, they will be given a warning.

4  The most ........................information is seen only by the CEO and his team.

5  We have a special ........................for recycling paper, but no sensitive information should be put there.

8  ........................data, for example details of payments to employees, is carefully protected.

9  The ........................door is always watched by a security guard.

11  Everyone wears an ........................badge with a photograph on it.

12  When you enter a ........................area, you have to sign in.

**6** **Match the sentence halves.**

1 You are more likely
2 When walking, men are more
3 I don't know if you're more or
4 If people think you're rich,
5 People disagree about whether taking vitamins decreases
6 There's no chance
7 70% of people in New Jersey
8 What are the odds

a own the home they live in.
b you'll be knocked off your bike if you walk.
c less likely to win the lottery or to be struck by lightning.
d of meeting your favourite singer?
e the odds of catching a cold.
f to experience identity theft if you don't use good computer security.
g the chances are they'll expect you to pay for things.
h likely to get knocked down by a car.

**7** **For each expression, choose the statement with the same meaning.**

1 There's a fifty-fifty chance.
   a The odds are even.
   b The probability is 75%.

2 The chances are 1 in 100.
   a The odds are 10:1.
   b The probability is 1%.

3 There's a one in four chance.
   a There's a four to one chance.
   b There's a 25% probability.

4 There's a 33⅓% probability.
   a There's a one in three chance.
   b The odds are 75:1.

5 There's a two to one chance.
   a The odds are 2:1.
   b There's a 75% probability.

6 Your chances are about 1 in 80,000.
   a It's likely to happen.
   b It's not likely to happen.

7 The odds against it are 100,000 to 1.
   a There is a .00001% probability that it will happen.
   b There's a 100,000 in 1 chance it will happen.

8 The likelihood is 1 in 2.
   a The probability is 50%.
   b It's very unlikely to happen.

# Answer Key

## Unit 1

**1**
2 design
3 install
4 working
5 installed
6 built
7 develops
8 involves
9 travel
10 installing
11 stay
12 travelling

**2** 2 g  3 f  4 c  5 h  6 b  7 d
8 a

**3**
2 'm
3 have
4 are
5 have
6 has
7 been
8 was
9 Did
10 was

**4**
2 ✔
3 She ~~don't~~ doesn't work on Fridays.
4 ~~Isn't~~ Doesn't he know he's not supposed to use his phone here?
5 ✔
6 ✔
7 I ~~doesn't~~ don't know how to operate the new equipment.
8 ✔
9 I'm ~~don't~~ not sure when the guys from China are coming.
10 I ~~not~~ don't have my laptop with me today.

**5**
2 Best
3 Just a quick note to
4 contact
5 regards
6 I'm writing regarding
7 please
8 confirm
9 Thank you
10 Attached
11 could you please be sure
12 let me know

**6** 1 c  2 c  3 b  4 d

**7** b  Order number 99032: shipping delay
c  Corrected order (replacement parts)
d  Re: 100 cases of paper?!
e  Short break

**8** 2 a, b, c  3 e  4 d  5 a  6 c

## Unit 2

**1**
2 48
3 5
4 38
5 130
6 85
7 14,085
8 60
9 24–36
10 125

**2**
A 2 How much does it cost? d
  3 How much does it weigh? a
  4 What's the fuel tank capacity? b
B 1 What are its dimensions? d
  2 What's its operating time? b
  3 What's the maximum load? a
  4 How high can it fly? c
C 1 What type of fuel does it use? d
  2 What type of engine does it have? b
  3 What's its maximum speed? c
  4 What's it made of? a

**3** 1 B  2 A  3 C

**4** 2 f  3 e  4 a  5 c  6 b

**5**
2 store
3 use
4 has
5 recharge
6 put
7 grows
8 damage
9 see
10 rotates
11 tells
12 plug

**6 Features:** It plugs directly into vehicle's DC outlet; It's very compact; It doesn't require cables; It has a built-in, ultra-bright LED light for night-time emergency roadside assistance; There's a 12-volt DC outlet to recharge mobile phone batteries; This tiny pill is actually an extremely compressed towel; When it gets wet, it grows into a 40 x 40 cm towel that you can use to clean up unexpected messes; The plug rotates through 360 degrees; An audible alarm tells you when it's time to replace it
**Benefits:** you don't have to worry about getting out of the car; it's easy to store; it's very easy to use; When it's dry, it's tiny and easy to put in your pocket or purse; Surge protection means dangerous power surges and electrical spikes won't damage your electronic equipment; Two blue neon glowing outlets make it easy to see and safe to use in the dark; making it easy to use in small or awkward spaces; you'll always be protected; Flexible outlets make it easy to plug in a lot of bulky plugs

**7** 2 f  3 e  4 d  5 b  6 a

**8 Across:** 3 options  7 warranty
8 Area  9 durability  10 coating
11 specifications  15 heavy
17 dimensions  18 quickly
19 resolution  20 benefits
**Down:** 1 source  2 Rotation
4 construction  5 operating
6 stable  10 composition
12 Capacity  13 capabilities
14 fastest  16 problems

# Unit 3

**1 and 2**
a  Make sure 2
b  When 5
c  First 1
d  Next 3
e  Finally 6
f  After 4

**3**  2 c  3 d  4 a  5 e  6 f

**4**  b 3  c 5  d 4  e 2  f 1

**5**  2 g  3 f  4 h  5 b  6 a  7 c  8 e

**6**  1  doorbell button
2  string
3  boxing glove
4  ball
5  trap door
6  pulley
7  chain
8  chute
9  weight
10  rope
11  hammer
12  cigarette lighter
13  flame
14  scissors
15  bell

**7**  2  This is the flame which burns the string.
3  The broken string releases the boxing glove which hits the ball.
4  There's a chute which the ball rolls down.
5  This is the rope which goes over a pulley.
6  The ball hits the scissors which cut the rope.
7  There's a weight which drops when the rope is cut.
8  There's a trap door which is pulled open by the chain when the weight drops.
9  Resting on the trap door there's a ball which falls when the door opens.
10  The falling ball hits a hammer which rings the bell.

**8**  1  squirts
2  ring
3  pivots
4  pushes
5  extinguishes
6  string
7  hits
8  loop
9  position

**9**  2  A bellows is a piece of equipment that blows air.
3  A blade is a flat cutting edge on a knife.
4  A tray is a shallow box which has no lid.
5  A gear is a wheel which has teeth.
6  A tank is a container that holds liquid.

# Unit 4

**1**  2 wipe  3 shield  4 dissolve  5 soak  6 prevent  7 run

**2**  2 L  3 C  4 L  5 C  6 P  7 C  8 D

**3**  2 freezing  3 peeling  4 rusty  5 noise  6 lubricated

**4**  2 e  3 g  4 h  5 a  6 d  7 b  8 c

**5**  b 1  c 4  d 6  e 8  f 3  g 7  h 5

**6**  a 6  b 8  c 1  d 3  e 5  f 7  g 2  h 4

**7**  a 5  b 3  c 1  d 4  e 2

**8**  is called; can be done; are processed; are traced; is carefully planned; is usually done; are placed; will be added; to be included

**9**  2  ✗
3  The machine that produces the new parts was designed by Philip.
4  The production process was explained by Eloise.
5  ✗
6  The questions at the end of the presentation were answered by Adam.
7  The contract was signed by Helen.
8  ✗
9  A successful year was enjoyed by all of us.
10  ✗

**10**  2  the right amount
3  the right amount
4  too much
5  not enough
6  the right amount
7  the right amount
8  too much
9  not enough
10  the right amount

# Unit 5

**1**  2  thank
3  take
4  nice to see
5  Sorry
6  Do you need a hand
7  appreciate
8  can I
9  Yes
10  Can
11  Yes, of course
12  could you
13  that's very kind
14  No problem
15  Thanks
16  It was a pleasure
17  was great seeing you

**2**  2 a  3 f  4 b  5 c  6 e  7 g  8 d

**3**  2 a  3 f  4 b  5 c  6 e  7 g  8 d

**4**  2  many
3  Few
4  the
5  some
6  several
7  all
8  another
9  a lot
10  other
11  a few
12  a little
13  couple
14  much
15  millions
16  any

**5**  2 C  3 U  4 C  5 U  6 C  7 U  8 C

**6**  2 j  3 g  4 i  5 h  6 b  7 e  8 a  9 f  10 d

**7**  2 T  3 T  4 F  5 F  6 F  7 F  8 T

# Unit 6

**1**  2  we won't be able to get our truck on to the site
3  we have to take it down ourselves
4  they've widened it
5  they'll have to widen the door
6  I won't let you come to work tomorrow

**2**  2 g  3 h  4 a  5 e  6 c  7 d  8 b

**3**  2  I'll walk
3  If the bus isn't on time
4  I'll get to work on time
5  I stop at the café on the way
6  I'll see a friend and forget about work
7  If I'm late for work
8  I'll keep my job
9  I get to work early
10  I'll lose my job

**4**  2 a  3 c  4 b

**5**  2  most
3  much lower
4  most
5  slightly higher
6  smallest
7  much more
8  best
9  worst
10  better

**6**  2 F  3 T  4 T  5 F  6 T

**7**  1  reusable
2  junk
3  drive
4  buying

5 mower
6 other
7 insulation
8 home
9 fewer
10 turn
11 products
12 environment

**8** Students' own answers

## Unit 7

**1** 2 g  3 i  4 p  5 q  6 k  7 s  8 o  9 v
10 j  11 d

**2** 2 can't
3 Can
4 should
5 need
6 have to
7 mustn't
8 shouldn't
9 don't have to

**3** page 4 b
page 5 c
page 6 e
page 7 d
page 8 a

**4** 2 e  3 b  4 d  5 a  6 f

**5** 2 a bicycle telephone
3 a two-year guarantee
4 an electric toothbrush
5 a three-wheel car
6 a two-metre sandwich
7 a newspaper boat
8 a diamond ring

**6** b 7  c 5  d 8  e 1  f 3  g 4  h 6

## Unit 8

**1** 2 a  3 a  4 a

**2** 2 F  3 T  4 T  5 T  6 T  7 F  8 F

**3** 2 f  3 e  4 g  5 c  6 a  7 b

**4** 2 e  3 f  4 a  5 c  6 d

**5** 2 He was waiting for Dumper 673 to arrive so he could repair its air-conditioning unit.
3 His GPS and radio
4 Derek Jenkins
5 Dumper 568
6 when Dumper 568 began backing into bay 49
7 Dumper 568 backed over and destroyed it
8 No one
9 the GPS and radio signal strength was too weak to transmit

**6** 1 tightened
2 was tightening, slipped
3 was talking, paying attention

4 talked
5 paid attention, followed
6 were following, lost
7 was losing

**7 Across**: 1 faults; 4 signs; 7 step; 8 trained; 10 talk; 12 controls; 14 intersections
**Down**: 2 tripped; 3 fire; 5 safety; 6 strain; 9 explosion; 11 ladder; 13 trip

## Unit 9

**1** 2 f  3 d  4 e  5 c  6 b  7 a

**2** 2 cloth
3 cable tie
4 cable tie
5 a
6 seatbelt and duct tape

**3** 2 i  3 e  4 h  5 c  6 f  7 b  8 d  9 g

**4** 1 Present Simple
2 *can*
3 Past Simple
4 *could*

**5** 2 phone box
3 work
4 built-in
5 scary
6 what if
7 gave up
8 filter
9 transporting
10 bicycle

**6** 2 If my company outsourced, it would save money.
3 If I had free time, I'd read books.
4 If I bought a car, I'd have to buy petrol, too.
5 If I won a lot of money, I wouldn't quit my job.

**7** Students' own answers

## Unit 10

**1** 2 saws
3 vibrating
4 cooking
5 burning
6 drawing
7 carving
8 plans

**2** 2 e  3 f  4 a  5 d  6 b

**3** a 4  b 5  c 1  d 2  e 3
f 2  g 1  h 5  i 3  j 4

**4** 2 NA  3 NA  4 A  5 NA  6 NA
7 A  8 NA  9 A  10 A  11 A
12 NA

**5** 2 got used to
3 used to
4 getting used to

5 used to
6 use to
7 ('ll) get used to
8 gets used to
9 used to
10 used to

**6** 2 b  3 c  4 a  5 b  6 b  7 a  8 c
9 a  10 c

**7** 2 c  3 d  4 i  5 j  6 h  7 g  8 e  9 f
10 a

## Unit 11

**1** 2 a  3 f  4 c  5 d  6 b  7 d  8 c
9 d  10 c  11 b  12 d

**2** 2 solve
3 converse
4 astronauts
5 alien life
6 artificial
7 traditional
8 limb
9 average
10 carry on
11 environmentally friendly
12 manned

**3** 1 g  2 f  3 c

**4** 2 h  3 f  4 a  5 g  6 e  7 b  8 d
9 c  10 i

**5** 2 b  3 e  4 h  5 g  6 f,i  7 d  8 j
9 a

**6** 2 can
3 can
4 should
5 'll
6 'd
7 'll
8 should
9 'll
10 'll
11 can

**7 Across**: 1 terrible  6 conserve
8 starving  12 compass
14 exhausted  16 filthy
17 vehicle  18 freezing
19 furious  20 extremely
**Down**: 2 enormous  3 survive
4 boiling  5 mirror  7 excellent
9 alternative  10 tiny  11 spark
13 aluminium  15 shelter

## Unit 12

**1** 2 b  3 b  4 c  5 a  6 a  7 c

**2** 2 We don't seem to have received a roll of wire.
3 It looks like you (have) sent only two boxes of dust masks.
4 There might be too many pairs of safety goggles.
5 You seem to have used the

wrong PO number.
6   It looks as if you've put in the wrong kind of filters.
7   There doesn't appear to be a wire brush.

**3**  b   We'll exchange them for the correct ones right away. 6
c   I'll send you two more boxes tomorrow. 3
d   We'll sort out a credit right away. 1
e   My mistake! I'll send you a new invoice. 5
f   I'm sorry about that. I'll add one to your next order. 7
g   The driver will collect the extra ones tomorrow. 4

**4**  2 k   3 m   4 h   5 a   6 c   7 f   8 b
9 e   10 g   11 j   12 i   13 l   14 n

**5**  2   gets
3   go
4   went
5   getting
6   gone
7   goes
8   got
9   want
10   could

**6**  2 d   3 b   4 f   5 a   6 e

---

## Unit 13

**1**  2   been done
3   have been removed
4   can be removed
5   be finished
6   be installed
7   been connected
8   been turned on

**2**  2   The cars have been moved.
3   The crane can't be brought in.
4   The power has to be turned off.
5   The roof should be finished.
6   The solar panels should be installed.
7   Yes, they were connected yesterday.
8   No, it hasn't.

**3**  2 a, d   3 c   4 c   5 c   6 b   7 b
8 a   9 c   10 a, d   11 e   12 b
13 a, d   14 c   15 a   16 c   17 a, d
18 c   19 e   20 e   21 e   22 a
23 a, d   24 a   25 c   26 c   27 c
28 c   29 c   30 b   31 c

**4**  2   doing environmental research
3   meteorologist
4   chemist
5   computer networking
6   a rural community
7   setting up a website

**5**  2 d   3 f   4 j   5 i   6 c   7 a   8 e   9 g
10 h

**6**  2   I've worked for AMX for five years.
3   I lived in Newbiggin from 2012 to 2017.
4   I've lived in Arbuckle since 2018 / for three years.
5   I started studying Chinese in 2015 / five years ago.
6   I've studied Chinese for six years.
7   I left TTD in 2015/five years ago.
8   I didn't study Chinese before 2015.
9   I don't work for TTD now.
10   I live in Arbuckle now.

**7**  2 T   3 F   4 F   5 T   6 F

**8**  2   was
3   are
4   can
5   should
6   can't
7   have
8   won't

**9**  2   The sheet metal press is being assembled.
3   The sheet metal press hasn't been wired in yet.

---

## Unit 14

**1**  2   question mark
3   parentheses
4   comma
5   brackets
6   full stop
7   slash
8   capital letters
9   period
10   exclamation mark
11   hyphen

**2**  2 T   3 F   4 T   5 T   6 F   7 T   8 F
9 F   10 T   11 F

**3**  2   closing bracket missing
3   full stop missing
4   commas missing
5   capital letter missing at beginning of sentence
6   full stop instead of question mark
7   apostrophe missing in doesn't
8   slash instead of hyphen

**4**  b 5   c 8   d 9   e 7   f 4   g 12   h 10
i 6   j 11   k 3   l 1

**5**  2   allows
3   easy
4   isn't
5   underfloor heating
6   underfloor heating
7   are

8   any

**6**  2 e   3 b   4 e   5 a   6 b   7 a   8 a
9 e   10 c

**7**  2 j   3 b   4 k   5 l   6 c   7 g   8 d   9 i
10 f   11 a   12 e

**8**  2   Five plus five equals ten.
3   Four times ten is forty.
4   Ten divided by two equals five.
5   One from eight leaves seven.
6   Three fives are fifteen.
7   Six into twelve makes two.

**9**  a   hairline
b   eyebrows
c   chin
d   shoulders
e   palm
f   arms
g   elbow
h   armpit
i   foot

**10**  2   4 cubits
3   2.4 palms
4   one cubit
5   4.8 palms
6   3 palms
7   9.6
8   3.2

---

## Unit 15

**1**  2 a   3 b   4 b   5 a   6 b   7 a   8 b

**2**  2   opposite
3   R&D
4   between
5   boundary
6   in front of

**3**  north-east

**4**  2 e   3 b   4 a   5 f   6 l   7 c   8 j
9 i   10 g   11 h   12 k

**5**  2   find
3   make
4   Set up
5   maintain
b 3   c 1   d 2   e 5

**6**  2 F   3 F   4 T   5 T   6 F   7 F

**7**  2   We can get rid of those boxes later.
3   Let's hold onto that plastic sheeting.
4   Do you want me to sort through the tools?
5   The system is hard to figure out.
6   The labels keep falling off.

**8**  2   take care of them
3   sweep it up
4   sort them out
5   sort it out
6   clean it up

**9** **Across:** 4 come 6 rid 9 look
12 through 14 take 16 clean
17 away
**Down:** 1 see 2 work 3 figure
5 get 7 around 8 throw 10 onto
11 check 13 tidy 15 keep
**Separable verbs:** clean up,
put away, work out, figure out,
throw away, check out, tidy up,
keep up

## Unit 16

**1** 2 Can
3 It would also be good
4 Would you like
5 Is there
6 I'm attaching
7 There will be
8 Please confirm

**2** 2 e 3 c 4 a 5 d

**3** 2 We'd like to meet you to talk
about the specifications.
3 I'm attaching some
information for our meeting
tomorrow.
4 Let me know if you need
more information.
5 A replacement nozzle will be
sent to you today.

**4** 1 filler cap
2 piston
3 push rod
4 calliper assembly
5 brake fluid reservoir
6 master cylinder
7 brake line
8 disc

**5** 2 T 3 F 4 F 5 T 6 T

**6** 2 d 3 e 4 f 5 f 6 c 7 d 8 a 9 e
10 c

**7** b 2 c 3 d 8 e 1 f 9 g 4 h 5
i 10 j 7

**8** 1 spring
2 blade
3 gear
4 funnel
5 belt
6 spirit
7 fuse
8 syringe
9 chain
10 lens
11 gauge
12 pulley
13 fan
14 rollers
15 sprocket
16 compass
17 identifying parts

## Unit 17

**1** 2 has been
3 is
4 will have been
5 will
6 had

**2** 2 F 3 F 4 F 5 T 6 F 7 T 8 F

**3** a 7 b 4 c 2 d 8 e 5 f 3 g 1
h 6

**4** 1 Liam
2 Update the budget
3 Adam
4 Visit the Singapore office
5 Prepare the drawings
6 Susan's
7 Production's
8 Go on holiday

**5** 1 c 2 c 3 b 4 d 5 b 6 c

**6** 3 d (glass tumbler)

**7** 2 c 3 e 4 f 5 d 6 b

**8** 2 h 3 f 4 d 5 b 6 g 7 a 8 e

## Unit 18

**1** 2 a 3 e 4 b 5 f 6 h 7 c 8 g

**2** 2 c 3 a 4 b 5 a 6 b 7 b 8 c
9 b

**3** 2 Cameras
3 phones
4 security
5 Visitors
6 guards
7 Prototypes
8 photos

**4** 2 Sam should have handed in
his phone.
3 Jan should be accompanied
by a security guard.
4 Gill shouldn't uncover the
prototype.
5 Gus isn't allowed to take a
photograph.

**5** **Across:** 2 hacking 3 access
6 documents 7 network 10 audit
13 consultants 14 rubbish 15 key
**Down:** 1 unlocked 4 confidential
5 bin 8 financial 9 front
11 identity 12 secure

**6** 2 h 3 c 4 g 5 e 6 b 7 a 8 d

**7** 2 b 3 b 4 a 5 a 6 b 7 a 8 a

# OXFORD

UNIVERSITY PRESS

Great Clarendon Street, Oxford OX2 6DP

Oxford University Press is a department of the University of Oxford.
It furthers the University's objective of excellence in research, scholarship,
and education by publishing worldwide in

Oxford  New York

Auckland  Cape Town  Dar es Salaam  Hong Kong  Karachi
Kuala Lumpur  Madrid  Melbourne  Mexico City  Nairobi
New Delhi  Shanghai  Taipei  Toronto

With offices in

Argentina  Austria  Brazil  Chile  Czech Republic  France  Greece
Guatemala  Hungary  Italy  Japan  Poland  Portugal  Singapore
South Korea  Switzerland  Thailand  Turkey  Ukraine  Vietnam

OXFORD and OXFORD ENGLISH are registered trade marks of
Oxford University Press in the UK and in certain other countries

ISBN: 978 0 19 457542 3

Printed in China

This book is printed on paper from certified and well-managed sources.

ACKNOWLEDGEMENTS

*Text sources*: p7 www.bbc.co.uk; p58 www.wikipedia.com; p61 www.about.com.

*Illustrations by*: Peter Bull Art Studio pp7, 25, 29 (angle grinder), 32, 36, 49, 59, 64,
65 (fanciful device); Martin Cottam p65 (boffin); Cyrus Deboo pp14, 21, 28, 69;
Mark Duffin pp9, 15, 17, 27, 29 (safety icon), 35, 39, 48, 51; Bill Ledger pp13, 22;
Ben Morris pp11, 20, 60, 72; Garry Parsons pp3, 16, 24, 30, 37, 67, 68, 70.

*The publisher would like to thank the following for their kind permission to reproduce
photographs and other copyright material*: Alamy pp8 (Vespa/Motoring Picture
Library), 41 (conference/Ed Maynard), 52 (aid work/Jacky Chapman), 58
(Vitruvian man/Interfoto Pressebildagentur), 64 (Ducati/Motoring Picture
Library), 73 (woman/Radius Images, password/Alexander Fediachov), 74
(lottery ticket/Imagebroker); Corbis pp31 (lifting boxes/Roger Ressmeyer,
forklift/Image 100), 44 (computer/Boeing 247); Elizabeth Whiting Associates
p50 (garden/David Markson); Getty pp12 (Koi carp/Photonica), 19 (couple/Taxi)
23 (engineers/Aurora), 32 (giant truck/Stone), 42 (two men/Digital Vision), 45
(motorbike/Conica), 56 (underfloor heating/Dorling Kindersley); Kitfox Aircraft
p8 (plane); OUP p16 (man), p54 (pyramids); Photolibrary Group pp26 (lawn mower/
Stockbyte), 28 (airport/Harry Vorsteher), 44 (Internet conference); Solent News
and Photo Agency p8 (car); MPI Offshore Ltd p7.

*Cover image by*: F. Schussler/PhotoLink/Photodisc courtesy of OUP Picture Bank

*The author would like to thank his editor, Anna Gunn, for the skill and experience she
brought to the project.*